RISE OF THE TIME LORDS:

A GEEK'S GUIDE TO CHRISTIANITY

By Michael Belote

© 2012, Lulu Publishing (1st Ed.)

© 2020, Amazon Kindle Direct Publishing (2nd Ed.)

DEDICATION

To my wonderful wife, Jessica, for her unending love and support;

and to my son Alex, for his unending curiosity;

and to my son Ryan, for his unending joy

TABLE OF CONTENTS

INTRODUCTION

I was a geek before it was chic.

I have always been a geek, and I am completely fine with that. Just don't call me a nerd or a dork: those are fighting words.

Being a child of the late 80's/early 90's, these three words have very specific meanings to me. A nerd is someone who is very smart and obsessed with learning knowledge for its own sake, often ending in social awkwardness; I can remember hearing a nerd defined as, "Someone whose IQ is higher than his weight." Steve Urkel from *Family Matters* was a nerd. Being a nerd is not cool. Being a dork is even worse: a dork has the nerd's social unacceptability, but without the brains. Screech from *Saved by the Bell* was a dork.

Geeks, in the 90's school terminology, were kids who were as smart as the nerds but lacked (some) of the social pariah status. We were still not exactly the cool kids; but everyone got along with us despite our occasionally non-mainstream areas of interest (comic books, old films, physics, etc.). Our TV hero was MacGuyver: the ultimate geek who refused to use guns because he knew he could beat the bad guys via creativity, knowledge of engineering, and an awesome mullet.

Unlike the nerds, who studied just for studying's sake, we geeks were only interested in how studying could make the world cooler. The nerds studied during physics because they wanted to get straight A's; the geeks studied because we wanted to understand the warp drives on *Star Trek.*

While nerds loved science for the sake of science, we geeks were always more into science fiction: what could the world be like if we could harness the powers of nature? We wanted to explore time and space with The Doctor from *Doctor Who*, or travel to the future with Marty McFly in a DeLorean, or help Kaylee get the engines running in *Firefly*. We were Mulder from the *X-Files*; the nerds were *The Lone Gunmen*. (If you get that reference, we are likely to get along well in this book.)

Another difference between nerds and geeks is that geeks generally have one area of pure obsession in their geekiness. There are film geeks and band geeks and fantasy geeks and comic book geeks. As for me, I was always a science fiction geek. Some of my favorite books growing up included things like Bradbury's *Martian Chronicles*, Lewis' *Space Trilogy*, Clarke's *Odyssey* series, Asimov's *Foundation* series, and basically anything written by Michael Crichton. I can remember many days of sitting beside my parents' pool reading the *I, Robot* books during hot summer days.

So it was probably no surprise to anyone when I ended up in engineering as a career. It was a natural fit for me. I was great at math and science, but I definitely had an engineer's mindset; while scientists spend their hours studying the "as-is" world, we engineers spend our time imagining the "will-be" world. Scientists study space because they are passionate about learning; engineers study space because we think it would be cool to strap three men inside a giant metal tube filled with explosives and try to park them on the moon.

When I was in college, I once heard a joke which describes the difference between scientists and engineers, nerds and geeks. A physicist and an engineer were challenged to race and see who could calculate the volume of a horse the fastest. The physicist ran off to find a large pool of water, into which he would dunk the horse and measure the water displacement to calculate the volume. It took half a day to get an answer. The engineer sat down with a notepad and his slide rule, and had the answer in five minutes. The professor was shocked, and asked how he got such a quick result. The engineer answered, "It was simple! First I assumed that the horse was a sphere...." This is how engineers work. We do not need an exact answer, just a "horse is a sphere" answer which is practical and solves the problem to an acceptable error level. Then we can move on to the next cool problem.

When I became a born-again believer, my natural tendency was to apply my geekiness to my newfound faith. Imagine my frustration when I realized how few geeks were writing Christian books! It seemed as though one side of the Christian bookstore was filled with slickly written books which took Biblical stories out of context and turned Jesus into a peddler of self-helpism; the other side of the bookstore was filled with brilliant theological textbooks. If I wanted to study Christianity, I either had to learn from the charlatans or the nerds. The nerds had the monopoly on Christian theology: their writings were brilliant, deep, logical...and lacked the imagination and creativity I so desperately desired. Where was the theology for the Whovians (*Doctor Who* fans, for the uninitiated)? Where was the theology for the Trekkies and the *Macguyver* and *Quantum Leap* lovers? Where was the Gospel written in a way which would excite those of us who learned about Einstein's relativity for fun?

Just as nerds made great scientists, they made amazing theologians; but there was nothing there which excited me and made me want to read more. Sure, there were some "science and the Bible" books, but they tended to come in two forms: books which pitted science against the Bible, and books which tried to harmonize science and the Bible.

Yet when I studied my Bible, this was not how I saw the Biblical authors approach nature. Rather than trying to debate for or against the local scientific beliefs of the day, people in the Bible seemed to see God's creation as a way of *explaining* the spiritual world. Nature was something of which to be in awe (Ps 19:1), and to use as a parable about the spiritual world (e.g., Matt 6:26-30, Matt 13, Mark 4:1-8,13-20, Mark 11:14, and many more).

I badly wanted a book which did not focus on resolving (or affirming) tensions between science and Scripture, but instead used the knowledge of nature to teach us things about the spiritual world. Just as Jesus used the growth rate of a mustard plant to teach about the Kingdom of God, I wanted a book which explored how gravity and quantum physics and heat transfer could teach us about spiritual things. After all, if the same God created the natural and spiritual worlds, then we should have (quite literally) an entire world of examples to help us learn more about our spirituality.

I never found that book. So I decided to write it.

In this book I will not argue for or against any particular theology or scientific theory. Rather, I will use modern science, engineering, and sci-fi concepts to serve as illustrations of the way God works in the spiritual world. As it turns out, there is a lot of Christianity with which geeks can become fascinated, but neither the shallow self-help books nor the tomes of theology are the method by which they will learn to love the faith.

Nerds (i.e., theologians and scientists) beware: in this book, I do a lot of assuming that horses are spheres. The scientific topics and theological topics which I will discuss in a mere paragraph could be studied for years by those wishing to know every detail about it, and I am glad God made such people. This book is not written for them. This book is written to all of my fellow geeks, and our goal is to see theology in just enough depth that we can understand the wonderful weirdness of how God works through us and with us.

In each chapter, I will open with a story about my life as sci-fi geek or some story about science or engineering, and each of these stories will then be used to describe a topic of Christian theology. In these pages you will learn about the Trinity from a Pringles can, about sin from star formation, about the Gospel from materials engineering, about the duality of man from Schrodinger's Cat, about grace from air conditioners, about heresy from atomic physics, and about judgmentalism from Einstein's relativity.

And when it is over, I hope all of my readers (geek or not) will have a greater appreciation for the Great Engineer, and what He has done in us and for us.

– ONE –

CALCULUS III, PRINGLES CANS, AND EXTRADIMENSIONALITY

When I first went to college to be an engineer, I thought it would be easy. Maybe this was naïve of me, but I honestly thought I was pretty awesome stuff. After all, I had breezed through high school with a 4.2 GPA on a 4.0 scale (which may seem a bit mathematically suspect, but that's another topic for another day). I was the best in my class at AP chemistry and physics. As a junior I made a 31 on my ACT, good enough for a full ride plus some spending money, so I never even bothered to re-take the exam as a senior (when I undoubtedly would have done even better). I arrogantly thought that I could ace my way through engineering without ever missing a Razorback football game.

So as I sat down in Calculus I on the first Monday of college, I was feeling pretty good. Until our teacher decided to prove a point. The teacher had us raise our hands if we were math, engineering, or physics majors – it was everyone in the class. She then had us keep our hands raised if we were honor students in high school – again, the whole class. She had us keep our hands raised if we were Chancellor's Scholars – perhaps two thirds of the class still kept our hands up. Then she had us keep our hands up if we had at least one year of calculus before this year – about half of the class kept their hands up...and mine went down.

You see, I had opted to skip Calculus as a senior in high school. I was a bit of a math whiz, and I was already taking AP Physics, so I figured why not take it easy? I had fulfilled my math requirements, so I might as well enjoy my senior year, right?

My first day in Calculus, I began to regret that decision. Because for the first time in my life, I was surrounded by an entire classroom of people equally as bright as I was, and half of them had the advantage of already knowing the material.

The teacher told us that the rest of us would struggle just to get by. Around midterm, she would start teaching us how to do the Calculus shortcuts; until then we had to do everything by long-form, while those who already knew the shortcuts could check their work more easily than the rest of us.

She was right, it was far more difficult than I had imagined. I fought and struggled to get a C. I had never even flirted with a B in my life. My first semester (since I had arrogantly taken 17 hours of hardcore engineering and math classes), I narrowly kept a 3.0 to avoid scholarship probation. It took everything in me to keep my scholarship in my second semester.

By the time I reached Calculus III, though, I had found my groove and was excelling above most of my peers. I found the subject fascinating. We started studying multivariate calculus. In particular, we spent a tremendous amount of time on studying the mathematics of complex curved surfaces like saddles.

Our professor (whose name, sadly, I cannot remember) was a jolly Scotsman who wore shorts and flip-flops regardless of the cold, and described everything using food metaphors. When describing motion along curved surfaces, he would always talk about his imaginary ant named Esmeralda, who would walk across the surface and describe her path. One day, while confusing us with a particularly complex path for Esmeralda, he mentioned the book *Flatland*.

Never having heard of the book, I followed up after class and his description intrigued me. This very short book, titled *Flatland: A Romance of Many Dimensions*, was written by a teacher named Edwin Abbott in the 19th century and was used to describe the concepts of multi-dimensional thinking. Flatland is a two-dimensional world populated by various shapes from geometry class. The narrator, for example, is a square; women are line segments; soldiers are triangles; hexagons are nobility, etc. The circle is the 'perfect' shape, and so the more one approximates a circle, the higher his social status.

Within Flatland, they only have access to two dimensions, which we would call "x" and "y." So when they speak of something being "up," they cannot conceive it as being "out of the page," as we would; instead, "up" means, "toward the top of the page." Because of this, all of their science and mathematics are limited by being trapped within these two dimensions.

For example, a Spacelander (like you or I) can see the entire "page" of Flatland all at once. When we view the narrator, we clearly see that he is a Square. Further, we can see both inside of him (into his "guts," as it were) and outside of him (his "skin" being the four lines that make him a square), at a glance. We can also see the nature or shape of every other being in Flatland at a glance. Why? Because we can look down from our third dimension, and thus see everything in their two-dimensional world from a superior vantage point.

A Flatlander, however, cannot at a glance tell who they are looking at, because they are limited by being inside Flatland. So if someone in Flatland walks up to Mr. Square, all the observer sees is a line—whichever side of Mr. Square is facing him at the time. It is impossible for him to know whether he is viewing Mr. Square, or a Triangle at an angle, or a Line from the side. The only way to know is to approach their Flatland neighbor and feel them physically while walking around them. Then and only then can it deduce the form of the other person. (I would imagine that this makes detective work rather difficult on Flatland: "No officer, I was not molesting that woman! I just thought she was my wife, and I had to feel all over her to know for sure.")

Yet, even a two-year old Spacelander can glance at the page and say, immediately, "That is a Square." Some knowledge which would be unobtainable by even the wisest Flatlander is simple and obvious even to a fool or a child from Spaceland. Being three-dimensional creatures, we have a much different perspective of their world than the Flatlanders do.

The book *Flatland* is completely fascinating and well worth a careful read for any geek. It offers an intriguing description of our world today. With the advances of modern physics, we now believe that the universe is not simply the three-dimensional world that we can perceive: we appear to be three-dimensional beings living in a universe of at least four and possibly as many as twelve dimensions! So while we consider how laughably foolish the Flatlanders are at trying to understand our third dimension, we find ourselves in the same predicament when challenged to picture the fourth (or higher) dimensions.

Think about some of the weirdness of being confined to a lower dimension. Take out a piece of paper, and let's call this your Flatland. (Seriously, do this, don't just read about it. It will make more sense this way.) On your paper, draw several dozen shapes. Now let us imagine that each of these is a person.

My, what a powerful god you must seem to them! Not only did you create them with minimal effort, but you are omnipresent, for you are able to see and interact with all of them momentarily, even if they are on opposite sides of the world! You are able to erase one and redraw him in another spot instantly. You are able to see not only their outsides but also what is happening inside their skin. You can see their true nature (shape, circle, triangle, etc.) at a glance, with no "feeling" investigation.

Imagine the miracles you can do for this two-dimensional world. Go grab a Pringles can from your pantry. (If you do not have a Pringles can, shame on you. They are delicious. Grab some other cylinder and it will have to do.) Place the can on your Flatland. When they examine this gift, what do they see? Draw around the parts touching the paper and you see what they see: a circle – because this is the only part which crosses through their page. As two-dimensional beings, they can only perceive of a single flat cross-section of your Pringles can at a time.

Now, flip the can on its side. Trace the edges which touch the paper again to see what they see. They now see a rectangle—the height and width of the can.

You see, a lower-dimensional being (like a Flatlander) cannot possibly "see" all of a higher-dimensional being (like a Spacelander). All they can see is the cross section which touches their world. If we step into their world they see not a boot but a footprint.

Now let's have some real fun. Pick out one of your shapes to be your "prophet" to Flatland; this is the shape who will try and explain about you to the other shapes. Try and think of a way to explain to the Flatlanders that these two drawings of the Pringles can are, in fact, the same shape: both a rectangle (with which they are familiar) and the circle (with which they are familiar) are actually the exact same object. They will of course think you are crazy! It is a fun thought experiment: get a friend or spouse or yourself (if you lack friends and spouses) and one of you pretend to be the Flatlander prophet. Try and explain to the prophet, using only words which they understand, that the Pringles can is both the circle and the rectangle simultaneously. It is impossible. They end up taking the whole silliness on faith, or rejecting you as a lunatic teaching fairy tales.

+ + + theology: the Trinity + + +

As we geeks begin our journey into understanding some of the fundamental theologies of Christianity, we should begin with trying to understand something about God Himself. From the very beginnings of Christian theology, there has been a battle over the nature of God. The Old Testament was as clear as it could be that there was only one God. God hammered this concept into the Israelites for centuries. Then along comes Jesus. He is the best Jew anyone has ever seen, and does amazing miracles to boot. He claims to be the Messiah, the savior prophesied in the Old Testament. In front of a few of His disciples, He transfigures miraculously; later He is put to death for blasphemy because He claims equality with God. After He dies, His body mysteriously disappears and hundreds of His disciples, from all areas of the countryside, claim to see Him again. Then He tells the disciples that He is sending them God's Spirit, a being and person, to live within them and advise and counsel them.

So from the start, Christians have had this very strange view that God was three unique persons—God the Father (the Jewish Yahweh), God the Son (Jesus, God in the Flesh), and the Holy Spirit (present at Genesis 1:2 and later dwelling inside believers). This was really, really confusing. And it caused a lot of debate in the early church.

In fact, this is one of the most common things that the first Christian creeds were written to clarify. Century after century during the Roman Empire, Christian leaders all gathered together, debated, and issued creeds stating what Christianity believed. What these bishops came up with is something like the following definition:

1. There is only one God.

2. This God has three Persons making it up: Father, Son, and Spirit.

3. These Persons have identical natures; all are equally God.

4. All are of the exact same substance.

5. All are co-eternal and co-equal.

Quite a few people throughout history, upon seeing this list, have had reactions ranging from, "Say what?" to, "You're insane." Skeptics call the above logically impossible; Christians call it a mystery.

I agree that it is a mystery, but not nearly as much of one as we may think.

Let us return to our Flatland for a moment. We all remember that we Spacelanders, as three-dimensional beings, have different perspectives from our two-dimensional creations. We see things that they do not see. So when we look at our Pringles can, we can see that this shape (which we engineers would call a "three dimensional solid") is neither a circle nor a rectangle, as the Flatlanders think of them. Rather, to use engineering terms, we would say that the can is a circular cross-section which has been extruded into the third dimension, resulting in a single, coherent solid. If you take a two-dimensional cross-section you see a circle; if you take a two-dimensional slice along the long axis, you see a rectangle.

This is demonstrable to any Spacelander, and quickly obvious to any engineer who has had to sit through an engineering graphics class and draw blueprints. In engineering graphics, we represent a three-dimensional solid on our prints using a top view, a side view, and a front view. By looking at these flat drawings and using our understanding of the third dimension, engineers can picture the Pringles can and instantly see how it is both a circle (top view) and two rectangles (front view and side view) while still being only one object.

But try explaining this to a Flatlander, after they examine the blueprint. What they will see is one circle and two rectangles (side and front). When you tell them that this is all one object, they will think you are crazy. In the end, after talking to you, they will end up summarizing your ridiculous claims with some list like this:

1. There is only one Pringles can.

2. This Pringles can has three Persons making it up: Mr. Circle, Mr. Front Rectangle, and Mr. Side Rectangle.

3. These Persons have identical natures; all are equally the Pringles can.

4. All are made out of the exact same substance.

5. All came into existence at the same time and all are equally part of the Pringles can.

6. Pringles are delicious.

Sounds familiar, doesn't it?

We, too, are trapped in our dimensional perceptions. We are three dimensional creatures, capable of full perception of up/down, left/right, and in/out. We also are aware of a fourth dimension, time, but only vaguely: we can only experience one moment in time in our minds. So just as the Flatlanders are two dimensional beings who, at any given moment, can experience only one cross-section of the Pringles can (a "three dimensional moment," if you will), so too are we three-dimensional beings who can only experience one cross-section of the fourth dimension (a "fourth dimensional moment"). That is why we can feel and experience "now," but cannot feel or experience the past or future. Like the Flatlanders, we only have access to a single cross-section from the next-highest dimension.

And yet, we find from the Bible that God created this entire universe, including time. So God is something more than a four-dimensional being. It is only natural, then, that we will be just as limited in understanding God's universe (let's call it Timeland) as Flatlanders are limited in understanding our Spaceland.

So when Christians speak of a Trinity, think of your Pringles can, and how it is at every moment both a circle and two rectangles. You cannot remove the circular cross-section or it is no longer a Pringles can; nor can you remove the rectangular extruded length and maintain its identity as a can. It must always be both at the same time, or it ceases to be a "can," by definition. This confuses Flatlanders because of their perspective: they cannot see anything but a two-dimensional cross-section, so it seems ridiculous to them to speak of something more than two dimensions. After all, their "nature" is two dimensions: anything more, by definition, is "anti-science" because it is unobservable and, therefore (by their definitions) supernatural.

Yet Pringles cans exist, don't they? They are actually real in the natural world and scientifically observable. It is not that the Pringles can must be accepted by "faith": no, it can be directly observed and proven...if you have access to the correct perspectives and dimensions. But since their perceptive abilities are limited by their access to two dimensions, the Flatlanders of course must use some form of faith combined with evidence in order to accept the very-real Pringles can.

How foolish would a Flatlander scientist seem if he pridefully refused to consider the teachings of the Pringles priests, because they referred to knowledge outside of his two dimensions of perception? Is he doing something admirable by self-imposing a handicap which limits his ability to understand reality? No! It is the upmost foolishness to say, "Since I cannot measure it, it does not exist." But of course, let us not be too hard on the Flatlander scientist, because here in Spaceland scientists often do the same. Saying that they are only interested in "natural" things, they reject any branch of knowledge which cannot be based entirely upon things available to our three dimensional measurements. As a result, they are handicapped and guarantee that they will never see the "entire" truth. The best that they can do is develop a reasonable theory to explain the three dimensions which they can directly access, just as the best Flatlander scientists can do is explain the two dimensions which they can directly access.

Ultimately, though, the Flatlander has good evidence of circles and rectangles; they have good evidence that miracles are going on, with circles and rectangles changing into one another; and they have a word from a Spacelander, from which they derive their strange doctrines of this "Pringles can" being circle and front rectangle and side rectangle, all at once, yet at the same moment retaining the identity of a single solid object.

We are in the same situation as Christians. We are told that God is somehow to us like the can is to Flatlanders: God is Father and Son and Spirit all at once, distinct persons but one Being. We cannot comprehend this—not because it is incomprehensible, but because *it is simply outside of our perspective and capacity for observation at this time*. As three-dimensional beings, it is impossible for us to picture a fourth-dimensional being; much more so, a fifth (or whatever God is). Only the greatest of mathematicians have even the foggiest understanding of multiple dimensions above our own, and theirs are abstract comprehensions only, which may have no basis in reality. For someone to actually attempt to describe a five-dimensional being...well, that is just as impossible as describing the concept of a "can" to a Flatlander.

So can I describe the Trinity? Not really, no more so than anyone else. But what I hope I have shown is that just because a higher-dimensional Being is unexplained does not make Him *unexplainable* or untrue. Indeed, if God *is* a being of greater dimensions (and He is, based on the Scriptures and the logic that He must be greater than this universe He created), then we know that He could only reveal Himself to us in three-dimensional parts and concepts at a given moment. Like the Flatlanders viewing the Pringles can, we can only see one "cross-section" or one Person of God at a given moment.

And this is what we see in our Bible, as it turns out. Some people (e.g., Adam, Eve, Enoch, Moses, and the Prophets) interact directly with the Father and have experiences with Him as Lawgiver and Covenant-Maker and loving creator of mankind. Other people (the disciples, John the Baptist, Pilate, etc.) have experience with the Son, seeing a flawless Jew who does mighty miracles and dies to reconcile us to God. Yet others (the Apostles, Paul, church members today) interact with the Holy Spirit inside of them, guiding them through divine inspiration. Because God is greater than our dimensions, our three-dimensional world cannot hold all of Him any more than you can make a Pringles can fit completely inside Flatland: it is a logical impossibility, for you cannot take a higher-dimensional object completely into a lower-dimensional reality without destroying what it is.

The best that we can do for understanding the Trinity is the same exercise that the Flatlanders must go through: we study each of the individual Persons (Father, Son, Spirit) to the best of our abilities; and we fuzzily understand that these three beings connect together in some fundamental way.

In some way that our three-dimensional minds cannot possibly ever picture, these three unique Persons are at the same time one single Being, one God, indivisible yet still individuals.

A Trinity.

– ONE POINT FIVE –

THE THREE BODY PROBLEM

+ + + author's aside + + +

Originally, I published this work in 2012. I was humbled to hear from several people like me—geeks wanting to explore Christian thinking—that it was helpful and interesting. Life moved on, and I largely forgot about it.

In 2020, I was asked to do an in-depth teaching for a regional staff of a major ministry. I spoke on the topic of Biblical justice, and a great time was had by all. (Or so I like to think.) At the end of the talk, my host—who has used my book in his ministry with geeky kids whom he mentors—mentioned the book. Those in the audience were excited to buy it. So imagine my shock when I saw that the paperback version was listed at $47!

I didn't write this to make money, and have always listed my books at minimal pricing. But I could not adjust the price: apparently, the transition between online publishers and the length of time since the first printing had led to the few remaining copies becoming high priced. So now I had to download the original book, reformat it to the new digital standards (a lot changed digitally between 2012 and 2020!), and re-release it.

I decided if I would do that, I might as well throw in a bonus chapter that I had always wished I had added.

And so...here it is.

+ + + The Three Body Problem + + +

Imagine that you are in a perfect vacuum. Nothing exists, anywhere.

Now add a sphere to this mental image. (In physics, we call this a "body"—something with mass.)

What happens?

Well...nothing. Life is pretty boring, actually. By Newton's First Law, unless an outside force acts upon it, this sphere will just sit here, floating, for eternity. Yawn.

Let's make it more interesting. Let's add a second body. Imagine now two spheres in your space. What will happen?

One of two things, depending on your initial conditions.

The first possible result occurs if you place the two spheres without any velocities. If the two spheres are stationary, then eventually Newton's Law of Gravitation tells us that they will slowly begin to attract one another. Given enough time, they will get closer and closer until they collide. Nothing ever happens moving forward: now you have two clumped spheres together, reminding us of the one-body situation.

The second possible result occurs if you place the two spheres in motion relative to one another. If the motion is fast enough, then they will separate, and you've got two "one body" situations again. If the motion is slow enough, then their gravitation will attract together and you get the same two clumped spheres. But if the velocity is between those two extremes, you will get a stable pattern of movement: the two will orbit one another.

This orbit is perfectly, completely predictable using even high-school physics. We know exactly where the objects will be not only in two minutes, but in two thousand years. As long as nothing else interferes, it is a simple, perfectly-predictable situation.

Now: let's add a third body.

What do you think will happen? With one body, we saw nothing. With a second body, we got very basic level of physics interactions, easily understood by a high school physics student. Both were completely predictable to the nth decimal place. So it would be logical to conclude that adding a third body will make things a bit more complex, but still predictable, yes?

That is not at all what happens.

Adding a third body into the equation does something completely unique: so much so, that in physics they call it the "Three Body Problem."

The three bodies *should*, we would think, interact through a combination of Newtonian forces and be able to be predicted mathematically. But it turns out, we can't.

For some reason, having a third body makes the system completely unpredictable. Unlike the two-body or one-body scenarios, there *is* no closed mathematical prediction model. In the entire history of math, there have only been one or two setups of three-bodies that can be predicted mathematically.

You might be thinking, "Well, what's so odd about that? Lots of things are unpredictable: my d20 rolls randomly at Dungeons & Dragons, that is how random things work!"

Except: the three bodies don't act randomly.

They form a pattern—often a quiet beautiful pattern, such as that shown by a Chinese research team below:

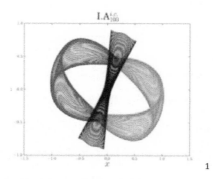

1

---

[1] Li XiaoMing et al., (2017). "More than six hundreds new families of Newton periodic planar collisionless

The Three-Body Problem is a bit like the famous Butterfly Effect, wherein a butterfly flaps its wings in the Amazon and leads to a thunderstorm in Africa: many systems in nature are *chaotically unpredictable*, and yet still follow a pattern and form that clearly show laws and natural order are at work.

We can map individual solutions for a particular set of three bodies if you know every detail accurately, but we cannot find a general equation or set of physics equations which allow us to predict with any accuracy how these systems will behave.

+ + + theology: the Trinity, take two + + +

The Pringles Can analogy from Chapter One has been immensely helpful to me, and I have heard from many readers that it was helpful for them, as well. The basic mystery of how "three" can be "one" in any meaningful way is difficult to wrap our heads around, and the Pringles Can analogy helps us achieve that.

But, like all analogies, it has its limitations.

If you stretch that analogy too far, you can end up with a heresy called Modalism. In Modalism, the three Persons of the Trinity lose their Personhood: they become merely "modes" or "masks" of the One God. So for example, a Modalist would say that Jesus did not really *return* to the Father and *send* the Spirit: as He is all of these at once, He simply "changed masks"—

---

three-body orbits." *Science China Mechanics & Astronomy*, 60: 129511.

like swapping avatars on a video game. A few people have read my Pringles analogy and taken it to this extreme, and in doing so they misunderstand the Trinity: they understand how three become one, but they lose the "threeness" of God.

This is where I think the analogy of the Three-Body Problem can help.

If God were merely one Person, then it changes our view of Creation in significant ways. A single Person—the lone Body in an empty void—is in a state of perpetual dullness. Nothing happens, nothing exists. Creation can be seen as an act of lonely desperation: God creates us because He is lonely and *needs* us in some existential way. Taken to an extreme, God *owes* us: before we came along, there was no one to play with.

The situation does not get much better if we add a second partner. A dualistic God takes on one of two forms: either the two clump together and are really indistinguishable, or they rotate each other like hunter and prey, or a dog after its tail, for all creation. This is something of the image we get with Zoroastrianism, or in Brandon Sanderson's *Mistborn* trilogy, with God and Satan serving as Preservation and Ruin, chasing each other in a steady, predictable, and endless orbit.

But if there is a third…things become more interesting.

The addition of a Third Person creates an infinite interplay between them. It is like jazz: there is an overall beautiful structure and pattern, but it is unpredictable, improvisational. As CS Lewis said in *Mere Christianity*, "[I]n Christianity God is not a static thing—not even a person—but a dynamic, pulsating activity, a life, almost a kind of drama. Almost, if you will not think me irreverent, a kind of dance."

The Pringles Can helps us see how the "three" can come from "one." But the Three Body Analogy shows us how the "one" can only exist with the "three": without three bodies, the beautiful, improvisational pattern never arises. The Triune Godhead becomes something unlike any other religion has ever attempted to describe: a single, dynamic, pattern of love sustained by three unique Persons in an endless relationship.

This aspect of the theology of the Trinity has a fundamental impact on our Christian worldview. If God is really this type of Three-Body God, then the very fabric of our universe is woven by a Being who has, as His fundamental truth, what Scot McKnight calls a *fellowship of differents:* a community made of different persons choosing to engage in perfect harmony together, to make the "jazz" of the universe.

And so when the Scripture tells us that He wishes us to be *like Him* and to reside *with us* for all eternity, we see in the Trinity what this looks like: an eternal drama in which a countless group of unique believers have chosen to dance together with God in patterns which are beautiful and impossible to predict.

And it also, therefore, gives us a vision of the Church: while we await this future reality, we act out this dance within our churches. By accepting of different Christians with different political views, races, philosophies, experiences, languages, and so forth into the unity of a spiritual family who loves and cares for each other and works together to do God's justice in the world, we give the world a picture of who God is.

A Trinity. Three bodies in one.

– TWO –

HOW ENGINEERS ROLL

If you are reading this book, you are likely a bit of a geek and also a Christian. After all, the subtitle of the book is, "A Geek's Guide to Christianity." (You can't teach logical skills like mine. You have to be born with them.) Some of you, like me, may be engineers. If you are not an engineer, you may look at those of us who are with a mixture of appreciation (we do build the bridges you drive over, after all), and pity (we are generally geeks, after all).

Believe me, I get it. I am self aware enough to know that we engineers are a strange bunch. I am a middle-aged man who, for every Father's Day and birthday, receives LEGO sets from my sons because from what they can tell, LEGOs are my favorite thing in the world. I read physics books on beach vacations. I have the XKCD comic website bookmarked and have read every Dilbert I can find. I love to DVR shows like *How It's Made*, and I used to serve as an expert reviewer for the website *www.howstuffworks.com.* I'm the kind of person who (as my wife is fond of saying), is incapable of telling you the time without first explaining how to build a clock.

So I get it: we engineers can be a bit *off.*

We are the men and women standing in the gap between the abstract world of scientists and the concrete world of welders and construction workers. The scientists want to understand the world as it is; we want to re-design the world as we wish it would be. And we not only take this approach home with us, we bring it with us everywhere. It is how we view the world. At all moments, at any time, we are engineering something. We are trying to invent.

This is just how we roll. An engineer cannot *not* engineer.

I love the book *Cheaper by the Dozen*, about two of the original industrial engineers, Frank and Lillian Gilbreth. It tells the story of these two efficiency experts and how they ran their home; it was written in 1948 by two of their twelve children. They ran their home like one of their factories, because they simply could not help engineering. Having family time was difficult with so many children, so they instituted a family whistle: when the whistle was blown, you immediately stopped anything you were doing and gathered for an assembly. Sometimes you received gifts. Sometimes punishments. But one time, the practice saved their lives, as the entire huge family managed to evacuate their burning home in less than fifteen seconds.

Not wanting to waste a moment of the day, records of French lessons were played for their children during tooth-brushing time. Morse Code messages were painted on their vacation home walls. They invented many other innovative social experiments, often ending with hilarious results in the book. The parents, being natural engineers, could not help themselves. With twelve children they saw a perfect chance for some engineering at home, and they took it.

I think every engineer is like this in some way. I know some engineers who rebuild cars or houses. I know engineers who build elaborate LEGO sets or model trains. I know engineers who create elaborate worlds in SimCity or other simulation-based video games. I myself have been known to buy Madden and NCAA Football, spend countless hours building a 30-year long dynasty, and never actually play the game—only simulate and world-build the entire time. And I think every engineer I know has ordered a whole host of tools for his house that he has not yet found an excuse to use, but thinks one day he might. Engineers cannot not engineer. It is just who we are.

One of my good friends and mentors in engineering, John, lives in North Dakota. Ever since I started working at the same company as John, I had heard him talk about going home on the weekend to work on his shop. He spent literally years building this workshop. Earlier this year, after having heard countless stories about his shop, I was sent to North Dakota on business. John and I met for dinner one night, and since he had nothing better to do he wanted to show me his now-completed shop. I had no other plans, and he was beaming like a proud father. So we rode out to his shop.

As we pulled up to the land, John proudly recounted countless details and engineering specifications. He told me the exact slope of the land that he had, and who owned it before him, and what precautions were needed if the nearby river flooded. He told me the history of where he got his dirt and how he prepped the ground. Then we arrived, and we walked inside... to a shop that is the same size as my house.

This shop was nearly 2000 square feet, with showroom lights (he told me how many lumens, but I forget) reflecting off the painted and speckled concrete floor. He had four vehicles parked inside, in various states of repair. Generally the things inside were from John's youth, and he was repairing them using only tools and equipment which were germane to their era – just because he could. In one corner was an oven which he bought for curing chemicals, or so he claimed. In reality, he bought it and fixed it up because it was from the fifties, and was the first "set it and forget it" oven with its own cooking timer, which he thought was cool.

Then John proceeded to tell me all about how he built the place, using nothing but himself and occasional help from his son. He refused to use any heavy equipment or serious help, using hand tools. (I think his precise rules were something like, "No tools that weren't available in the 19th century.") Why? Well, because he's an engineer. And that's the kind of thing that an engineer does – spend three years building a shop using the most painfully awkward equipment possible, just to see if he can do it.

This is engineering. We just do things differently than other people. That's how we roll – we want to build and invent. We cannot help ourselves.

+ + + theology: cosmology + + +

God is an Engineer.

Why do I say that? Let me give you several reasons.

1. He creates things that He doesn't have to, with little purpose other than the fun of creating them.

The ancient Jews and Christians knew that the heavens and earth were something glorious, and that as they learned more about nature, they would become more enthralled with its Creator. Psalm 19 famously opens by saying, "The heavens declare the glory of God, and the sky above proclaims his handiwork. Day to day pours out speech; and night to night reveals knowledge." (Ps 19:1-2, NIV). Every day that we learn something new about nature, David says, we have learned something new about God.

And one thing we have learned about God is that He is, above all else, a *prolific* Creator. For many centuries, we humans assumed that we were the center of Creation, and that everything revolved around us (both literally and figuratively). The more we see of the heavens, the more we realize how ill-founded this assumption was. God went around creating things that we will never be able to even see. He created things that are hidden to us and every descendent we will ever have. He made black holes whose power we can only observe indirectly. He made breathtaking supernovas in areas of space which we will never see. He made brilliant quasars whose beauty is hidden from us. He created extravagant solar systems which will be long gone before their light could even reach us. He created a universe far, far greater than we could have possibly imagined.

We live in a universe which, scientists believe, has a radius of some 46 billion light-years, a light-year being just shy of 10 trillion kilometers. This is a number so large that it is almost impossible to comprehend, so let me try and help.

Picture a single tiny grain of sand on the beach. Then imagine how many grains of sand it would take to lay side-by-side and stretch completely from one edge of the Earth to another. This is a huge amount of sand – about 63 billion grains. Visualize that in your mind's eye: enough tiny grains of beach sand laid side-by-side to stretch across the entire planet. Now imagine 580 *million* more of these strings of sand, all lined side by side. This is a huge number, right? Now imagine that individual tiny grain of sand—all 36 million million millions of them—is blown up to the size of the original Earth. Each individual grain of this impossibly long string of sand is blown up so that all of them are the size of Earth. This insanely huge string would *just barely* stretch across the universe.

In other words...the universe is big. Really big. Gigantic. Gargantuan. Why did God do all that creating? He can't have been doing it all for our sake, because the universe will die a heat death long before the light reaches us to allow us to view the majority of what He created. So why would God bother to create such a vast and glorious display, when humans will never even see it?

Because He was not creating it for us to begin with. He made it for Himself, because He is an Engineer. One of the biggest misconceptions people hold is thinking that all this around us exists because of us, not for His glory. He'll build what He wants to build, and just for Himself!

The same is true of life on earth. People ask why God would create the dinosaurs only to have them die off before humans came around. Well...why not? Dinosaurs are awesome. There has not been a warm-blooded boy in history who did not find the concept of dinosaurs enthralling. God created them because He wanted to. If I could create anything, I would probably create dinosaurs, too.

God is a creator who loves the act of creation itself. As such, He is going to create things for His glory and enjoyment whether we ever experience them or not. He does so for His joy, as an Engineer. The universe was created for His glory, not for our satisfaction.

2. He loves creating, and He knows all about Quality Control.

I love the depiction of the Creation in Genesis 1. What a description of engineering.

In Genesis 1:1 we see the Big Bang ("In the beginning, God created the heavens and the earth"). He creates time ("in the beginning") and matter ("the heavens and the earth"), all at once—just as modern physics teaches. But we find out in verse 2 that He does not yet put it into any kind of form or shape ("and the earth was without form and void"). So we have a creation filled with all of the matter which will ever exist, but it has not yet been shaped. During this shapeless time, God's Spirit was "hovering" above His creation; the word in Hebrew is *rachaph,* and it is also used in the book of Deuteronomy to describe a mother bird fluttering over her eggs. Engineers, is there any better description of how we invent? Do you not also "hover" over your projects like a mama bird does her eggs?

Then, He begins to give everything a form. Over the next thirty verses we see God put shape to everything in the universe. Every time He does so, He gives it a name and calls it "good." This, my friends, is what we in the engineering world like to call Quality Control. We not only create, but we are compelled to check our work to ensure that it meets our expectations.

And so God creates light, and sees that it is good. He creates the sky, and sees that it is good. He makes vegetation appear, and sees that it is good. He creates everything in an orderly fashion, and then eventually in verse 31 calls it "very good" before relaxing and taking a day off.

I do not think that anyone can truly understand the end of Genesis 1 and start of Genesis 2 better than an engineer. We are the ones who relate to the feeling of fluttering worriedly over a project, checking our work carefully as we go (muttering under our breath, "That's good, that's good"). When complete, we kick back on the deck with a nice cold beverage of our choice (Diet Mountain Dew, for me), and say with a satisfied sigh, "I see everything that I have made, and it is very good. Time to rest from the work that I have done."

3. He creates in different ways.

The death to joy for an engineer is coming into work every day and doing the same thing, over and over and over again. I cannot tell you how many engineers I've interviewed for jobs who were quitting their past employment purely out of boredom. They needed a new challenge. They wanted to learn something new and make something that they have never before made.

If as a boss you ever want to get rid of your engineer, just make his life all paperwork and repetition. He'll quit on his own and save you the severance cost of firing him.

It seems that God also liked to mix things up. In Genesis 1, creation was not described using the same Hebrew words in each act; rather, we are told three different levels of activity that God used: *bara'*, *asah*, and "it was so."

Some actions are described using the word *bara'*. This word implies divine intervention, a miraculous engagement in creation. God is getting involved to do something which has never been done before and cannot happen without His intervention. He does this in verse 1, at the Big Bang: "In the beginning, God created [*bara'*] the heavens and the earth." He does it again in verse 21, when life explodes onto the scene: "So God created [*bara'*] the great sea creatures and every living creature that moves...." And He does it again in verse 27, with man: "So God created [*bara'*] man in His own image, in the image of God He created him; male and female He created them." We can say with certainty that God intervened in miraculous ways during the Big Bang, the first appearance of complex life, and the creation of mankind.

But not every creation act uses this term. Other actions are described using the word *asah*. *Asah* is simply a generic word like "do"—God did something. It could be used for any kind of work. Maybe it means that God took something He already *bara'* created and shaped it into something new, like a potter shapes clay into a pot but does not re-create the clay itself. Maybe it means He established natural laws so that everything would happen in precisely the time and order He intended, in some sort of divine Rube Goldberg mechanism. (As an engineer, I can tell you that this sort of pre-programming is extremely difficult and immensely rewarding.) Regardless of which it is, the Bible says three times that God *asah* created things: the sky (v.7); the heavenly bodies (v.16); and the land animals (v.25).

So God *bara'* created some things and *asah* created other things.

But still God created a third category of things, and we are not told what He did in these cases at all. The Scripture simply says that He wanted these things to happen, and they happened. In Scripture, these are the "And it was so" verses. It does not say how God caused it to happen: was this a creation done through the Spirit, through angels, or through natural processes? Or is it just another example of *ex nihilo* (out of nothingness) creations? Who knows? All we know for certain is that Genesis describes the creation of light/darkness (v.3-4); seas/land (v.9-10); and vegetation (v.11-12) with the "And it was so" description.

We do not know exactly why Genesis 1 shows different "levels" of creative activity. It may be that God, like any engineer, enjoyed doing some things differently: some things He just divinely wills into being, others He shapes existing materials, and still others He accomplishes by programming natural laws and watching as the giant, universe-sized invention proceeds according to His plans. Perhaps the words are used simply as synonyms and we are reading too much into it. Regardless of our understanding of why He created with different levels of activity, we do know that...

4. *He was in control at all times.*

At the time Genesis 1 was written, this was one of the more groundbreaking statements. Other ancient religions generally saw time and the earth as pre-existent and in a state of chaos; the gods (the sky, sea, heavenly bodies, trees, etc) show up and fight each other, tame chaos, and in the process man is created (either by accident or as an afterthought). This is the way most ancient creation myths explain things, but not Genesis 1. In Genesis 1 there is one God only, and He creates both time and everything in the universe. The sun, moon, stars, and sea are not competing gods, but things which He made for His purposes. He made man with a purpose, and gave Him a job to be His regent on Earth. Genesis 1 seems to have no higher goal than to show the inherent foolishness in the religions of the ancient world, by proclaiming that there is but one God and that everything which was created was done under His sovereignty. There was no battle against other gods because no other gods existed. At no time was the future outcome in doubt; He always maintained control.

This is the primary difference between creationism and evolutionism. The evolutionist believes the development of life was random and unguided, while we believe there was a purpose. The evolutionist believes that any outcome was possible, including no life at all; we believe that life (and in fact, spiritual human life) was inevitable, because it was God's plan all along. The evolutionist believes all species evolved from a single-celled organism through random chance; the creationist believes God was always in control and randomness played no role. Theistic evolutionists, who stand with one foot in each of the two camps, argue that there was some evolutionary development which was random, but God intervened to control and guide the overall process.

The concept of creationism (that God was in control, and it was not random) is explicit in the text of Scripture. But it is worth taking a moment to clarify that "creationism" is a lot larger umbrella than the media makes it out to be. Generally when the media speaks of creationism, it uses the term incorrectly. There are, in fact, at least four major branches of creationism:

Theistic Evolution/Progressive Creationism: The belief that the scientific findings in biology, geology, and paleontology are essentially true and that God's role was to intervene miraculously to ensure that His desired result was achieved. Thus it is God "guiding" natural evolution.

Old Earth Creationism: The belief that there was no evolutionary role at all, no moment of randomness: God was in control of all stages of creation, but He did so gradually over billions of years. Thus Old Earth Creationists accept the findings of astronomy and geology, but reject evolutionary theory.

Young Earth Creationism: The belief that Genesis 1 should be literally interpreted and that the Hebrew word *yom* (usually translated "day," but at other times translated as "moment" or unknown periods of time) is a literal 24-hour day. Thus Young Earth Creationists reject any scientific finding which indicates an earth older than about 10,000 years, or a gradual development of creatures.

Cosmic Time Creationism: The application of Einstein's Relativity (see chapter fifteen for more on relativity) to the creation event. In this explanation, *proper time* as measured from an undilated clock at the universal center would register only six days as the *dilated time* of Earth (traveling at a very high speed after the Big Bang) would show billions of years. In other words, the earth would age billions of years during the passage of only a few days on an undilated, "cosmic" clock.

All four branches of creationism share a common trait, however: God was in control throughout creation. It was not random.

The Fine-Tuned Universe

Many people with a physics background find it difficult to come to any other conclusion except that there must have been a God. The commonly-used theological term is the *fine-tuned universe.* In our universe there are twenty or more fundamental constants which had to be exactly correct at the time of the Big Bang, or no life could have ever existed. And when I say exactly right, I mean balanced on an incredible knife's edge.

For example, if the ratio of electrons to protons at the moment of the Big Bang was different by even 1 part in 10^{37}, no life could have ever existed in the universe. The odds of this happening randomly are absurdly small. To demonstrate how unlikely it is that this would happen naturally, let us do another thought experiment. Imagine that I chose two people at random out of all seven billion people in the world. Further imagine that on each of these two people, I chose two random body hairs to color red. (Why I would do that, I don't know. In this example I appear to be a creep of some kind. Bear with me.) Now, let's say that you have *one* chance to randomly choose the same two people I chose. Then, you must randomly choose the same two hairs I chose, again on your first attempt. Then you need to sit down and play poker, and just by luck get dealt three straight royal flushes. Seem like a ridiculous scenario? It is. Of course this is absurd. Yet this scenario has the same odds of success as a randomly-correct electron-to-proton ratio.

Another example of such fine-tuning is the cosmological constant. The cosmological constant is a mathematical constant in relativity and quantum mechanics equations (in simple terms, think of it as a repulsion effect creating the rapid expansion of the universe). If this constant was different in one part per 10^{120}, no life could have ever existed in the universe. Again, let me use a thought experiment to demonstrate how ridiculously unlikely it is for this number to just so happen to be the right value for supporting life. Imagine that I am thinking of one random American right now. You get one guess, and must think of exactly the same person, just by random chance. Then you must roll a ten-sided die five times in a row, and have it just randomly happen to give you his ZIP code (in order). Then roll the same die again ten more times, and it must give you his phone number with the area code, also in order. Then sit down and play poker with him for three hands, and get three straight royal flushes. Then go to the golf course and hit nine straight holes-in-one. Then get struck by lightning...three times. All of those things happening randomly are just as likely as the Cosmological Constant being *just right* to produce life. It simply cannot happen by chance.

This is well known in physics, and is why physicists, engineers, and mathematicians tend to believe in God at a higher rate than life scientists, who do not study cosmology. Atheist Fred Hoyle once said that it looked like someone "has monkeyed with physics, as well as chemistry and biology, and that there are no blind forces worth speaking about in nature." Refusing to believe in God, Hoyle instead concluded that a race of superintelligent aliens were doing all of this monkeying.

Many other notable astrophysicists, such as Paul Davies, Frank Tipler, Alan Sandage, and Nobel prize-winner Arno Penzias ended up converting to either Judaism or Christianity, and all state that the fine-tuning of the universe was critical to their decision. Penzias went as far as to say, "The best data we have concerning the Big Bang are exactly what I would have predicted, had I nothing to go on but the five books of Moses."

Even atheists like Stephen Hawking admit this is a powerful argument. The only way they have come up with to get around it is to assume (with scant evidence, I should note) that there must be infinite multiple parallel universes. If this were true, they argue, then one such universe would have been guaranteed to have produced sentient life; and since we are sentient then we just so happen to be living in that one particular universe.

You may note that such a proposition is not a statement of fact but faith; it is complete conjecture, and seems to my mind at least to be implausible in the extreme. Much more plausible is that things in our universe do not appear random *precisely because they are not random*. They appear fine-tuned because the Great Engineer did indeed design the universe with a purpose.

God created prolifically because, as an Engineer, He loves to create. He kept checking His creation for good quality, and kicked back to relax in pleasure when He was complete. He created using a variety of different methods (*bara'*, *asah*, and "it was so"). And He remained in control at all times in His creation, always building towards His ultimate goal: to make a spiritual being. Man.

THREE

FAILED STARS AND FALLEN MAN

As engineering students, we of course take many required science courses, but even after several physics and chemistry classes, we must take some additional science electives. Most engineers at my university chose biology (which was deemed to be the easiest of the electives), but I chose Astronomy. Like so many sci-fi geeks, I have always been fascinated with astronomy. I was never really all that interested in star maps and memorizing constellations, though. Even as a teenager I was aware that constellations were meaningless things, unworthy of study. They only vaguely resemble anything, and then only because we happen to be standing on Earth: from any other vantage point they look like nothing at all, for the stars are all at different angles and distances. (My editor reminds me here that constellations are pretty to look at, so let me revise my statement: while poets and dreamers find constellations pretty to look at, the physicist rolls his eyes and considers them silly. Hopefully this makes the poets of the world feel better about wasting their time.)

No, my interest in astronomy was always the physics of it, the incredible science fiction stories which come from trying to understand how the universe works. Throughout my younger years I was fascinated by "hard sci-fi" books like Clarke's *Odyssey* and *Rama* series, which take great detail to work out their stories in precisely the manner in which physics would really work. The impact of the physics of the astronomical world fascinates me to this day. Very few things are geekier about me than this ongoing, boyhood obsession with stories about the stars.

As a student, one reason I loved Astronomy was how easily the laws and rules of physics could be applied and the sometimes strange consequences predicted. Biology and geology I always found less exciting because of their static nature: you were not predicting what might happen next, but rather trying to explain the rocks and fossils you had already found. This was not of great interest to me as a student. Chemistry was slightly better, but it was in physics that I found my joy. Predicting based upon known laws how far this trebuchet would launch a rock and then seeing if we were right, understanding how a curveball curves, repeating the experiments of Galileo and the astronomical observations of Copernicus and Kepler: these were the things which inspired me.

That is what makes space so much fun for a physicist: it is an intellectual playground. It is a vacuum so large and with such massive objects spread so far apart, the interplay of forces can be well understood, and the actions of the heavenly bodies easily predicted. It is not evolutionary biology, which is based upon random mutation rates and thus is inherently unpredictable; or geology, where you can only look backward and theorize about how rocks became the way they are; or chemistry, where minor laboratory mistakes and contaminations can make your results different than expected (and possibly turn you into a giant lizard super-villain, if we can trust the science of the *Spider-man* comics); or climatology, where even a supercomputer cannot process all the necessary variables to predict weather or climate with any sort of accuracy. All of these are wonderful sciences and well worth studying, but I just cannot "geek out" about them in the way I can physics and astronomy. For me, astronomy is wonderful because it is so reliably predictable; I am consistently amazed at how insanely accurately you can predict something *which no one has ever before attempted.*

An amateur with only a basic knowledge of physics and a cheap Wal-Mart telescope can predict and explain the motions of massive heavenly bodies to incredible levels of detail, discover new planets, and view starlight which has crossed the galaxy to arrive at your eye, having passed through a gauntlet of space-bending gravity wells and asteroids in its path. This absolutely enthralls me.

Take, for example, the formation of stars. There is no randomness or unpredictability at play in star formation: even though we cannot directly observe it (due to our short lifespans), we can know with mathematical certainty a series of events which could lead to a star's birth, and we can test each of these individual steps easily.

Using Hubble and other telescopes, we can see many dense nebulae in the galaxy, clouds of molecular hydrogen (H_2). The physics of what would happen to such a cloud of gas are straightforward and can be calculated by physics students very early in university. There are two competing forces which would play upon the gas cloud: an internal gravitational force pulling the cloud inward toward itself, trying to create a collapse, and an outward pressure force trying to separate the gas. As long as these two pressures are equivalent, nothing will happen. This is called *hydrostatic equilibrium*, and is the reason that we have air to breathe: the Earth's gravity is constantly tugging on the atmosphere to try and collapse it down to the ground, while the internal gas pressure in the atmosphere is forcing itself apart to try and fly off into space. Because these perfectly match, we have a stable atmosphere.

The same is true in a molecular gas cloud. As long as everything is perfectly balanced, nothing will happen. But sometimes, incidents occur. Clouds bump into each other. Nearby supernovae explode, pushing extra matter into the cloud. Tidal forces compress and agitate clouds.

When such an incident occurs, the gravitational force for collapsing inward becomes greater than the pressure force pushing outward. And so the gas cloud begins to collapse in on itself.

As the cloud collapses tighter and tighter, the temperature increases. Eventually the temperature gets so hot that nuclear fusion begins in the core, and a massive amount of heat and energy are released. Now not only are the gas pressures pushing outward, but the heat energy from the fusion also pushes outward, and a new state of equilibrium is formed. But this is not static equilibrium, it is dynamic: the edges are always moving, dancing back and forth in a sort of unstable stability, and as a side effect blast out huge amounts of heat and light into the universe.

And then, a star is born.

If you get your Wal-Mart telescope out, you can also see what happens when things are just slightly different from the above scenario. Imagine you have the gas cloud we originally discussed. The gravitational force is strong enough to start collapse, but the collapsing cloud is just *not quite* massive enough to become a star. It continues to collapse and collapse but eventually the gas pressures pushing outward are able to balance the gravity, reaching a state of equilibrium before fusion begins.

What would you get in this case?

Jupiter.

You see, Jupiter is essentially a failed star. The gas giant is huge (you could fit over a thousand Earths inside it), and is made of the same stuff needed to make a star. The gravitational pressure was strong enough to start collapse, but when the collapse started, temperatures rose and the gas tried to expand outward, fighting against the gravitational collapse. Eventually there was sufficient outward force coming from inside of Jupiter to create stability of form, *before* igniting into a star.

(Fun fact: Jupiter actually sends out more heat than it receives from the Sun.)

(Note: If you did not find that last statement to be a fun fact, this book might not be for you.)

So in a very real sense, Jupiter is a failed star. It reached equilibrium and stability before it could ignite.

+ + + theology: the Fall of Man + + +

As we saw in the last chapter, God's act of creating nature involved the creation of incredibly fine-tuned natural laws which even today we can use to accurately understand how the universe works at a mathematical level of detail. And so it should come as no surprise that the same God who created nature and imbued it with natural laws should also, when creating a spiritual being like man, implement spiritual laws as well.

When God created Adam and Eve in the Garden of Eden (Gen 2), He created them as spiritual beings. Inside of them were two competing forces, just as with our gas cloud example.

The first force I call *spiritual gravity*. It is the tendency of mankind to be selfish and self-centered: the tendency to see the world around us as bending inward toward us. Just as a planet bends the space-time around it creating gravity, so too do we see the world from a self-centered perspective and believe it should form itself to us. We see this in our children, from their very infancy, and unfortunately in all of us as we age. Spiritual gravity, left unchecked, makes our souls collapse inward in selfishness until all that is left is smallness and "me"-ness.

But inside all of us also is what I call *spiritual force*, something inside us that makes us want to be a "good" person. It makes us want to give to others, to sacrifice ourselves, to be in harmony with our fellow man and nature, and to achieve the goals that God has for us. This internal force is always challenging us and pushing us outward, encouraging us to put others before ourselves.

When God created Adam and Eve, they were a bit like a molecular cloud. They were in *hydrostatic equilibrium*: any "me-centered" spiritual gravity was more than offset by their internal goodness (which had been given to them by God). So their relationship with God was perfectly static: it did not move from good to bad given the time or their behavior. They lived in a period of peace and perfection.

And then, an Incident occurred. Just like a collision can lead to gravitational collapse of a molecular cloud, this incident would cause a major change in Adam and Eve's spiritual life (and the history of the world).

God had provided for Adam and Eve a rich and beautiful garden filled with anything they desired to eat, but off-limits was a single tree: the tree of knowledge of good and evil (Gen 2:16-17). God warned Adam that eating of the tree of knowledge would lead to his death. Theologians generally all agree that the "tree of knowledge of good and evil" is so named because eating of this tree would reveal to man the laws of God, and Adam would be aware of right and wrong.

Had Adam never eaten of this tree, he would have remained in a state of innocence and purity: not knowing the difference between good and evil, he would not be held to its consequences. He would remain in a state of equilibrium with God. But eating of it, and receiving such knowledge (a conscience) would lead to his spiritual death. Once he knew of the Laws of God, he would be unable to adhere to their principles and would knowingly sin against God. (We will discuss this more in chapter four.)

In Genesis 3, we see Satan enter the picture in an attempt to oppose God's plan for humanity. Satan sets out to destroy the equilibrium between God and man, and does so by playing upon the spiritual gravity of Eve: he makes the discussion all about her. In Genesis 3:4, the serpent says to Eve that God was lying to her, and that if she eats of the tree she will be "like God." Satan's lie to Eve is to tell her that God does not really want the best for her, that He is keeping her back from her true potential.

Satan rightly points out that God inside her was pushing outward, opposing her spiritual gravity: He did not want her to collapse inward on herself. Satan's lie was to imply that overcoming God's desire in this matter was a good thing.

So Eve eats of the tree. And then Adam eats as well. "Then the eyes of both of them were opened, and they knew that they were naked" (Gen 3:7).

Adam and Eve were now running purely on spiritual gravity, so they began to spiritually collapse. They severed the connection between their *spiritual force* and its source (God), and their lives were now run only by their willpower.

Just like a molecular gas cloud which has begun to collapse, the two began to change into something they were not originally intended to be. Their equilibrium with God was lost. This results in their exile from the Garden He made for them (Gen 3:24), and the curse of having to live in the wild world of Earth, which in turn means pain and suffering.

This event, in theological terms, is called The Fall of Man: it is the moment when we ceased to maintain our equilibrium with God and our spiritual gravity now is free to collapse inward on itself.

+ + + theology: original sin and sin nature + + +

Ever since Adam and Eve, we have inherited in our DNA this knowledge of good and evil, and are thus subject to spiritual death: that is, our own natural *spiritual gravity* (or self-centeredness and sinfulness) is greater than our *spiritual force* (our internal conscience/goodness inside us which pushes outward). Left to our own devices, we all will continue to collapse inward and can never again return to equilibrium with God. There have been countless economic studies which demonstrate that, even during our moments of charity, there is always a "me"-centered component, a part of us which is doing things not for the right reasons but the wrong ones. That is, we are always collapsing inward on ourselves, failing in sinful spiritual gravity.

All Christians agree on the nature of spiritual gravity. Now that we have within us the knowledge of good and evil, we find that spiritual collapse is inevitable, and this spiritual gravity is the only force which is under our control. Willpower is ineffective at making us perfect no matter how hard we try.

Trying harder to "be good" simply results, much to our frustration, in a faster collapse: the more pious we become, the more judgmental we become (which is a sin); the more we aim at doing the right things, the more we want to be lauded for our spirituality (which is a sin); the more we try to avoid sexual sin, the more we end up thinking about sex and lusting (which is a sin). We simply cannot, through our own efforts, overcome our natural tendency to collapse within ourselves.

The Apostle Paul said it in this way:

"I do not understand my own actions. For I do not do what I want, but I do the very thing that I hate….I have the desire to do what is right, but not the ability to carry it out." (Rom 7:15,18)

This is the sad truth of *spiritual gravity*. We may know what is right, but we cannot carry it out. Our own human nature shows that all of our actions (whether attempts to sin or to avoid sin) will always lead us to more sin. We collapse inward on ourselves.

All Christians agree with this, although they get in a number of theological discussions regarding the difference between "original sin" or "sin nature" or "ancestral sin." But this isn't a theologian's book, it is a geek's guide to theology—and geeks do not care about semantical arguments. From a practical standpoint, all Christians agree that our natural state is one which is out of equilibrium with God, unstable, and which always leads us to collapse inward on ourselves and to create something that God did not desire. All Christians agree that our works cannot lead us back into right relationship with Him.

For example, in 1999 the Catholic Church and Lutheran church signed a joint declaration stating their agreement on this topic: "By grace alone, in faith in Christ's saving work and not because of any merit on our part, we are accepted by God and receive the Holy Spirit, who renews our hearts while equipping us and calling us to good works." In 2006 it was also adopted by the Methodist church. This is essentially an agreement in what I call spiritual gravity by all parties: that our works only lead to collapse, and it is God who provides the opposition to our natural tendency to collapse.

All major Christian theologies are basically in lock-step regarding the nature of sin itself, at least from a practical standpoint: due to Adam's sin, we all inherit a nature which is rebellious against God, and inevitably (regardless of our greatest efforts) we collapse inward on ourselves into lives of sin.

In other words, left to ourselves, we are all bound for self-immolation: like a collapsing star, we become increasingly self-focused and increasingly sinful, collapsing down under the weight of our own spiritual gravity until eventually we ignite. Just as a collapsing molecular cloud's gravity overwhelms its internal gas pressure, resulting in a star being born, so too have our souls resisted God's desires to be right with us. Our self-centered sinful nature eventually ignites us in an inferno of sin.

All Christians agree that a life free from spiritual gravity is no longer possible. We cannot return to being dust clouds: Adam's sin started the cycle of spiritual death, a cycle which leads to internal combustion.

What God thus desires for us is to simply stop the collapse. Because of our choices, God cannot return us to molecular dust clouds, but neither does He desire for us to collapse into stars; the Bible says that God is not willing that any should perish, but that all should have eternal life through Him. So what God tries to do is to increase our *spiritual force*, the pressure which pushes against our own spiritual gravity. God wants us to become like Jupiter, a "failed star." He wants the internal pressure (coming from His grace) to push against our natural spiritual gravity, until a new equilibrium is met.

We cannot return to the pre-Adam equilibrium where we have no sinful natures. But we can avoid self-ignition, if the internal pressure from God's grace is sufficient to create a new equilibrium: a Jupiter situation, where we no longer ignite on fire but find that God's grace is able to match and overcome our sinfulness, and a new "thing" is created: a spiritual creature whose natural spiritual gravity is offset by the spiritual force of God's grace.

As we saw in the joint Catholic-Lutheran statement about our sinful natures, we have broad agreement within Christianity about the factual nature of both sin and grace. Where we disagree is about the transmission method by which we receive God's grace.

Broadly speaking, there are three basic theological approaches to explain where we get our grace: the Sacramental approach, the Reformed approach, and the Wesleyan approach.

The **Sacramentalists** (like Catholics and the Orthodox), argue that God gives us this spiritual force through the sacraments. In this view, it is properly-performed rituals which serve to convey God's grace to us, such as baptism, confession and penance, confirmation, and celebration of communion. So while they would agree that our moral good works have no bearing on avoiding our spiritual gravitational collapse, they would argue that the method of receiving God's grace is through the working of the sacramental act itself.

The **Reformed** (like most Protestant denominations, following the teachings of Luther and Calvin), argue for a concept called total depravity: that is, no action of ours (including partaking in sacraments) plays any role in receiving the grace of God. Reformed argue that our spiritual gravity is so overwhelmingly strong that only through God's miraculous intervention can we receive any spiritual "push" to oppose our own spiritual collapse. Some Reformed teach that your moral efforts might lead to rewards in heaven (others disagree), and some argue that you do still have some form of obligation in partaking of sacraments (again, others disagree); all Reformed, though, agree that you cannot contribute at all to the receipt of God's grace. He sends it to you of His own accord.

The **Wesleyan** approach is a third option, coming from the founder of the Methodist movement, John Wesley. Wesley argued that God's grace came into us in three waves. Everyone started out with some internal pressure to fight against the spiritual collapse; he called this *prevenient grace*. Therefore, we were not totally depraved; the spiritual gravity is not overwhelming but is sufficient for us to realize our inevitable failure to fight it. Next comes *justifying grace*, an offer by God to fill you with the full spiritual force to fight against spiritual collapse—an offer that each individual has free will to reject or accept. Finally comes *sustaining grace*, an ability to create one's own internal grace through holy living and fight against the collapsing gravity through one's willpower.

These are the three major branches of theological thought regarding God's grace. Ultimately we all agree that this grace is of origin in God alone; the big question theologically is, "How does it get inside us?" If our participation in certain Christian rites results in God's grace being placed in us, then the Catholics and Orthodox are right. If God's grace comes to us regardless of our own actions and purely because of the goodness and power of God, then the Reformed are right. And if God's grace is slightly within us at the beginning, and then becomes active in fighting sinful collapse due to our faith in Him, the Wesleyans are right.

Summary

Though at times the theology of the Fall of Man can seem strange to those of us without seminary degrees, geeks will find it useful to think of these spiritual laws in terms of the physical laws surrounding star formation.

A star begins as a dust cloud which is in a state of hydrostatic equilibrium, neither collapsing nor expanding. Due to some inciting incident, the dust cloud begins to undergo collapse due to the force of gravity. As it collapses further and further in on itself, the dust cloud's interior begins to heat up and a pressure force begins to push back against the gravitational force, seeking to expand the gas back to its original equilibrium. These forces do battle and ultimately there are two possible endings once collapse has begun: either the star will collapse until it self-ignites and consumes itself as a burning star, or a new state of equilibrium will be met (such as the formation of a gas giant planet like Jupiter).

The fall of man, it turns out, is remarkably similar. Man was in a state of equilibrium with God in the Garden of Eden, and all was well. Until one day an inciting incident occurred: man became aware of evil after rebelling against God and eating of the tree of knowledge. Man's spiritual gravity (his sinful nature) began to cause an inevitable collapse which, without intervention, would lead to spiritual death in an inferno. But God offers us a spiritual force within us, which He calls grace, to fight against and overcome this collapse. If His grace is not within us, we fallen men will continue our spiritual collapse, gravitationally folding in on ourselves in a selfish, sinful mess until we ignite; but with God's grace placed inside of us, the pressure of God pushes outward as an expanding force, stopping and then overcoming our spiritual gravitational collapse to form a new equilibrium.

– FOUR –

SUPPLY AND DEMAND AND PROHIBITION

One of the things which separates a geek from a nerd is that geeks often have an obsession with a particular genre of offbeat knowledge, and essentially become walking Wikipedia articles. There are film geeks and comic book geeks. There are fantasy literature geeks, some of whom have started a campaign for George R.R. Martin to "write like the wind," so that his series *A Song of Fire and Ice* (the basis of the HBO *Game of Thrones* hit show) will be finished before he dies. (I'm sure he appreciates the sentiment: "George, it would be sad if you died, but tragic if you died without finishing the books I want to read.") Jack Black played a music geek in *High Fidelity* and *School of Rock*. As I said earlier, I am a science fiction geek.

I have a friend named Joe who is a beer geek. Joe took classes at Michigan State in beer tasting. He has tried beers from all over the world to compare their qualities. He brews his own beer at home. He tours breweries for fun. He ordered potato chips from all over the world, and once spent months "pairing" the appropriate chips to the appropriate beers, like a chef might pair wines with meals. Joe does not receive any money for his obsession (in fact, it has cost him thousands). He receives no fame or honor. He just gets incredibly excited about it. Though not generally a geek in other ways, this is one area where Joe "geeks out."

One famous set of geeks are Steven Levitt and Stephen Dubner, the authors of the always-interesting *Freakonomics* books and blog. Economists by trade, they seek out the "hidden side of everything": the financial motivations which drive so many of our behaviors, often in unexpected ways. These books have some fascinating studies, particularly relating to parenting and the lack of actual impact "helicopter parenting" has upon the success of the child.

Having studied a very small amount of economics in college, and reading interesting books like *Freakonomics* and the works of Malcolm Gladwell, I have developed a bit of a soft spot for economics. It isn't sci-fi...but

I could see myself becoming an economics geek one day if I really went down the rabbit hole. I have not yet done that, but one of the aspects of economics which I have studied and found fascinating is called the *law of supply and demand.*

Most people have heard of the law of supply and demand, of course, but often they fail to understand the real implications on human behavior. Put simply, supply and demand says that in a competitive market, the price of something is directly related to how much of it the buyer can easily find (supply) and how badly the buyer wants to purchase it (demand). If supply increases but the demand does not change, then eventually the market will be "saturated" with more of the object than the buyers wish to purchase; the only way to sell the product is to continually lower the price until people are willing to purchase it again. If supply of an object drops (a shortage) while demand remains high, then the price of each unit will skyrocket as the rarity of the object makes it more valuable.

You can see this in the purchase of nearly anything, but my favorite example is an event with a stadium full of people, like a sporting event or rock concert. The seat price generally remains stable until the day of the concert. Then, if you are walking to the concert without tickets, you will no doubt see scalpers nearby: they have purchased tickets at the normal "reasonable" price in the hopes of re-selling them (illegally) at a higher price.

The scalpers are manipulating the laws of supply and demand to turn an easy profit. They know that if you have shown up and paid to park at a concert but have no ticket, your "demand" for the ticket is going to be pretty high; however, because the concert is sold out, the supply of tickets for you to choose from is very low. This drives the price per ticket up very high.

But then let the concert start and do the same walk. Perhaps thirty minutes after starting time, all of a sudden the same scalpers will sell you the tickets for almost nothing. Why? Again, supply and demand: the demand to attend a concert which is half over is very low, so they are stuck with a supply of product with little demand, lowering the price.

The moral? Stop paying for concert tickets. You hate the opening acts anyway, so just show up an hour after it starts and buy the tickets on the cheap from the scalpers. (Actually, that is probably illegal, so ignore this advice.)

Supply and demand may seem like a straightforward concept, but 19th century Christians failed to understand it, leading to an event which would have very much angered my buddy Joe, the beer geek. Starting in the 1820s, various American religious groups (most notably Methodists and Baptists) began a political fight for *prohibition* – the outlawing of alcohol in any form in the United States. It was called the "Noble Experiment," and had an astonishing cross-section of supporters: Northerners and Southerners, Democrats and Republicans, African-Americans and the Ku Klux Klan all banded together to try and ban the manufacture and sale of alcohol.

It was interesting that Christians were the driving force behind the Prohibition movement, because teetotalling was not the traditional Christian stance on alcohol. Prior to the 19th century, the Judeo-Christian stance on alcohol had been temperance ("use in moderation"), while the Muslim stance was prohibition ("do not use"). But rampant abuse of alcohol in the early 19th century was wreaking havoc on family lives; this, combined with the rise of tent-revival Christianity led to a wave of anti-alcohol sentiment. After the Civil War, bars began offering "free" salty meals at their bars; this is called a "loss leader," because they knew people would come for the free meals (on which the bar would lose money) and the saltiness would result in them drinking heavily (on which the bar would make profit). This further increased destructive alcohol abuse. Furthermore, drinking was commonly associated with the influx of immigrants and Catholics, and this bolstered the argument against alcohol for many of the Methodists and Baptists, who approved neither of the immigrants nor the Catholics.

The widespread support resulted in a new Constitutional Amendment. In 1920, the Eighteenth Amendment went into effect, making the sale or production of alcohol illegal. The politicians and leaders of the prohibition movement believed that this would lead to a new period of lower alcohol consumption and less crime. However, supply and demand economists could likely have predicted the result. The demand for alcohol did not diminish due to prohibition, but remained the same—everyone who used to go drinking still wanted to drink. However, the *supply* of alcohol fell drastically as the major brewers were shut down. This had two immediate effects: first, the price of liquor skyrocketed, such that the wealthy could still afford it while the poor and middle-class could not; second, the overall consumption of alcohol in the short-term lowered due to the lower supply.

However, consumption only lowered for a short time. Since demand remained as high as ever, and supply was so low, this created a tremendous market with huge profits if one was willing to break the law. Violations of the law were widespread, with people brewing dangerous homemade "moonshine" liquor. Most surprisingly, it led to the unexpected rise of the Mafia—an organized crime syndicate which leveraged its ability and willingness to break the law to build a massive and profitable criminal empire.

While alcohol consumption did indeed fall during the first few years of prohibition, before long alcoholism actually increased faster than ever before. Casual drinking was virtually eliminated by the ban, while binge drinking became prominent and wide-spread. Rather than reducing crime as expected, the Prohibition era saw a massive 24% spike in crime, including a 44% rise in drug addictions as people turned from alcohol to opium, heroin, and cocaine use. Those who were taking the risk of brewing alcohol, in an attempt to maximize profits, made drinks as strong as possible. Thus the percentage of drinkers who became drunk rose dramatically. Within fifteen years of the start of Prohibition, alcoholism had become so widespread that a Christian group founded Alcoholics Anonymous to help the ever-increasing throng of alcoholics in a supposedly "dry" era.

By 1933 the effects were so widespread, and the Prohibition so unpopular, that another amendment was made (the 21st), to repeal the 18th Amendment and return to the status quo. But why did prohibition fail? How did something so popular that it passed the rigorous constitutional amendment process fail so badly? It is shocking to consider that, within just a few years, a new amendment became so unpopular that it was able to be repealed by another amendment. How could something with such bipartisan popularity fail so quickly, and so spectacularly?

Ultimately, the failure came because of a lack of consideration for the laws of supply and demand. A desired behavior (in this case, consuming alcohol) can only be eliminated if either the supply or demand is utterly eliminated. Organizations such as Alcoholics Anonymous have a track record of success because they treat the individual so that he or she can control their desires (demand), and thus change the behavior. Prohibition aimed to eliminate the very existence of liquor (supply). But elimination of supply for an item which can be easily made in someone's home is realistically impossible. Prohibition failed because the teetotalers aimed at eliminating supply (which was, practically speaking, impossible) yet did nothing to address the high demand. Therefore, the result was not elimination of the alcohol but rather a thriving black market for it, which in turn increased crime in order to produce the supply.

Compare this to illegal drugs today. They also have a demand, and their supply is also limited, thus creating a black market just like the Prohibition era. However, the criminal effects of society from illegal drugs today (though bad) pale in comparison to the Prohibition of alcohol. Why? Because the demand for illegal drugs is relatively low in comparison to alcohol; in the time of Prohibition, virtually every family in America had at least one person who liked to drink. So when the black market developed, the resultant crime wave was massive and widespread. In fact, it was so widespread that within just a decade, the supporters of Prohibition had changed their stance completely, and now realized that Prohibition was a situation where "the cure was worse than the disease."

Though supply and demand is ultimately about economics, I see the same principles at work in our parenting. For example, my children's bedtime is always 8:30. Exceptions are only in the rarest of circumstances. As such, the supply of nights staying up late is very low, while the demand is always high (no kid ever actually wants to go to sleep). This in turn makes the value of staying up late quite high to our kids, and thus it provides a very strong incentive if they wish to "buy" a chance to stay up late with some exceptional behavior.

It works the other way, as well: all parents have seen that threats of punishment (time-outs, spanking, etc.) only go so far toward getting appropriate behavior. If it is possible to break a certain rule (supply) and the desire in the child is high enough (demand), then eventually they will pay whatever the "cost" in punishment might be in order to do it. At times, children are smart enough to only "pay the cost" where they are unlikely to be caught; I have seen many children who are angels around their parents, then transform into demons on the playground. Because the desire (demand) for the bad behavior was not removed, and the opportunity (supply) was available, then no amount of rules will stop the bad behavior.

Only when the child believes that the opportunity for doing wrong (supply) has been completely eliminated, or if their hearts are changed so that they no longer desire the thing/action (demand), will they actually obey even when they could otherwise get away with it.

+ + + theology: the uses of the Law + + +

In chapter two, we saw that God created man; in chapter three, we saw the rebellion of man and the advent of original sin. We all have a sinful nature because when Adam and Eve ate of the fruit in the Garden of Eden, their "eyes were opened" to the reality of good and evil. That is, they became moral beings. But why does becoming a moral being cause a sinful nature? Isn't knowing good and evil actually a positive thing? (That was the serpent's argument to Eve, after all—that knowing good and evil would make them "like God," which was something to be desired.) How does knowing the Moral Law cause us to have spiritual gravity, and for our works to collapse into selfishness?

This is not a new question. Indeed, the apostle Paul addresses this in his letter to the Romans:

> "Yet if it had not been for the law, I would not have known sin. For I would not have known what it was to covet if the law had not said, 'You shall not covet.' But sin, seizing an opportunity through the commandment, produced in me all kinds of covetousness. For apart from the law, sin lies dead. I was once alive apart from the law, but when the commandment came, sin came alive and I died. The very commandment that promised life proved to be death to me. For sin, seizing an opportunity through the commandment, deceived me and through it killed me. ...

For we know that the law is spiritual, but I am of the flesh, sold under sin. For I do not understand my own actions. For I do not do what I want, but I do the very thing that I hate. Now if I do what I do not want, I agree with the law, that it is good. So now it is no longer I who do it, but sin who dwells within me. For I know that nothing good dwells in me, that is, in my flesh. For I have the desire to do what is right, but not the ability to carry it out. For I do not do the good I want, but the evil I do not want is what I keep on doing.

Now if I do what I do not want, it is no longer I who do it, but sin that dwells in me. So I find it to be a law that when I want to do right, evil lies close at hand. For I delight in the law of God, in my inner being, but I see in my members another law waging war against the law of my mind and making me captive to the law of sin that dwells in my members. Wretched man that I am! Who will deliver me from this body of death?" (Romans 7:7-11,14-24)

Here, Paul says that we all want to do the right things in our inner beings (the right things being, "those things which are in accordance with God's moral law"). The fact that we desire to be "good" shows that the law is holy and pure. But simply our knowledge of evil causes our flesh to become fixated upon it, and to eventually fall into sin. To continue my analogy from chapter three, it is as though the law of gravity at first did not exist, so our "gas cloud" stayed in perfect static equilibrium. But as soon as the gas cloud becomes "aware" of the law of gravity, collapse is inevitable; it cannot be stopped. The exposure to the law is the thing which sets the inevitability into motion. In the same way, as soon as Adam and Eve were exposed to the law, they were now subject to failing before it.

Perhaps no one is better capable of understanding this than parents. When your children hear words, they repeat them as they see fit. Many words they do not repeat, some they do. No word has any particular power to them. If they hear a curse word, not knowing that it is a curse word, then it has no particular attraction. But as soon as they hear that the word is "bad," all of a sudden it has a special appeal to them. The fact that they have to be careful not to say it around mom and dad tells them that this word is special. The law has created sin in them.

Suppose that I tell you, "Don't think of a polar bear." You will fail. Because as soon as I said it, your brain actively thought of polar bears in an attempt to avoid thinking of polar bears. The presence of the law ("don't think of polar bears") results immediately in the sin. It is impossible to avoid.

We see the same thing happening in the world with regard to sex. For a long while, it was rare to share sexual details in public, polite society. Many people throughout history had little knowledge of "alternative" sexual lifestyles (at least compared to today), and as such the more "mainstream" sex was enough for them to be satisfied. But the rise of the sexual revolution and pornography (particularly of the Internet variety) has made people much more widely aware of deviant sexual behavior. As such, their exposure to these deviances (which before they would never even have imagined) begins to draw them sinfully toward it. Each deviant behavior viewed increases the desire to be a little "kinkier" in the bedroom. This satisfies them for a while, until they see something more deviant or bizarre sexually and then this new act becomes their fantasy or fetish. The very exposure to a sinful behavior, and the knowledge that it is wrong, makes it desirable.

To put it in terms of supply and demand, the chance to rebel against God was always present; God did not make us robots, and chose to give us the freedom to sin. Of course, Adam and Eve had this freedom before the Fall, too; but being unaware of this freedom to rebel, they remained innocent. It was only after becoming aware of the Moral Law that they realized what sin was, and that they were capable of sinning. This is why they remained perfectly sinless while running around nude in the Garden all the way up until the Fall: not knowing about sin, they were unable to have any sinful thoughts about one another. Like an innocent toddler, they ran around and wrestled and played nude, with no concern. There was no worry of sinful thoughts. Only after becoming aware of "right" and "wrong" did they become ashamed at their nudity and realize that they needed to be covered.

This, ultimately, is an issue of supply and demand. The availability to sin against God is always present; the devil makes sure that we are given a steady supply of temptations in this life. But remember our laws of supply and demand: if supply of something is large, it is not considered valuable while the demand remains low. Like our concert scalper an hour after the show started, temptations are not turned into sins when the demand for performing the sin is low. For example, it would be sinful for me to punch my neighbor in the face; but I rather like Lance, and have little desire to punch him. So although it is possible for me to sin (supply), I am unlikely to sin because the desire is not there (no demand).

What Paul is saying in Romans 7 is that before we became aware of the Law, the supply of temptations existed, but there was no demand to do them. Once exposed to the Law, though, the demand begins to rise in our flesh to perform the sinful behavior. (We even have sayings affirming this, like the common phrase, "Rules were made to be broken.")

In the Sermon on the Mount (Matt 5-7), Jesus says the same thing. For example, in Matt 5:27-30 He says that lust is the same as committing adultery: the two are the same sin. But how is that possible? How is looking at a woman on a computer screen the same sin as actually cheating on your wife with her? The reason is because even though you did not pay the cost (by doing the sin), or maybe the woman was unavailable (no supply), you still have the *demand* in your heart; the very presence of lust indicates that you would be willing to do that sin, if the "cost" were reasonable and if you had been given the opportunity to get away with it. If I look at a woman lustfully while driving down the road, then the desire which awakens in my heart is a demand for sin. The lustfulness inside of me (the demand) guarantees that there is a scenario (supply) in which I would gladly sin in adultery.

Jesus says the same throughout much of the rest of the Sermon on the Mount. Becoming angry is the same sin as murder, because the awakened demand in your heart means that, if the supply was available and the cost was right, you would commit murder. This is why He is so firm about not judging others, in Matt 7:1-5: because we all commit the very same sins in our hearts that we condemn others for committing. (More on this in chapter fifteen.)

So we see then that the Moral Law is more than just a list of "rights" and "wrongs": it actually awakens within us a knowledge of sin and, therefore, our own sinful capacity. In theological terms, we call this one of the "Uses of the Law." The Lutheran Book of Concord describes three uses of the Law:

1. To provide sufficient social and legal punishment to discourage disobedience;

2. To reveal to man his inherent sinful nature and inability to avoid breaking the Law; and

3. To provide the saved man with a fixed rule by which they can guide their lives.

John Calvin, in his *Institutes of the Christian Religion*, said essentially the same thing, but swapped numbers one and two. There is sufficient debate over whether the third use of the Law is actually valid, and indeed Martin Luther himself never stated this use (despite its current position in Lutheranism). But this debate is well outside of the scope of this book, which desires to get only into theology as far as is useful and practical.

Suffice it to say that, in terms of supply and demand, the two primary uses of the Law are: (1) to provide a very high cost for disobeying, thus making some unwilling to "buy" the sin; and (2) to reveal to man the "demand" inside his own heart, thus making him look toward Jesus as a source of salvation. Or, to continue the analogy from chapter three, the introduction of the Law both shows us where our spiritual gravity should stop in order for us to remain in equilibrium with God, and it also creates the inevitable result that we will fail to live up to the Law.

– FIVE –

MEET THE SIMS

In middle school, I once took a class for which, I now believe, our tax dollars should not have paid. I cannot remember its name (something like Industrial Technology or Industrial Careers), but it should have been called Geek Heaven. Anyone who attended Carl Stuart Middle School at that time and did not take this class missed out greatly. The (alleged) purpose of the course was to let us get an early understanding of what different careers were like, so that we could better shape our high school educations.

Maybe this purpose would have been achieved if our teacher had not been a coach whose preferred method of teaching was to read the paper and drink coffee all day while we ran around unsupervised. But though our parents may have thought we were learning valuable lessons about career paths, the reality is that we had a really cool one-hour playtime every day.

The class was held in a large open room with a smaller, soundproofed room to one side. Only a few desks were in one corner; the bulk of the room was arranged into stations, each of which represented a career. The students were divided into three groups, and we rotated every week or two from one station to the other, performing the activities in each station to learn about various jobs.

At the soundproofed station, we had simple audio equipment, microphones, and CD players which were connected to speakers in the main room. Our job here was to be the class DJ, introducing songs and putting together set lists. Supposedly we were learning about modern media; in reality we were listening to "The Thunder Rolls" by Garth Brooks about five times per class period.

Other stations had even more dubious connections to real jobs. The electronics station had those LEGOs with electric motors which you could use to make cars and helicopters. The engineering station was where you built a matchstick bridge and tried to see who could build the longest and strongest.

The physics station was a homemade rocket kit. One station had Microsoft Flight Simulator, a video game which they justified letting us play by calling it "training" for an airline career. Another station had a car racing arcade game where you drove at breakneck speeds through crowded city streets, trying to avoid pedestrians. I cannot remember what career it was supposed to introduce; taxi driver, maybe? Oh, never mind: we were supposed to *avoid* pedestrians, so that can't be it.

Needless to say, this class was absolutely awesome.

My favorite station of the whole class (even beating the LEGO station, which is hard to achieve) was the "City Planner" station. Did we study population growth and utility needs and methods of discouraging crime and civic leadership at this station? Of course not. We played SimCity.

Kids today cannot understand the joy of a geek playing SimCity back in the early 90's. SimCity was one of the most revolutionary games of its time. While most games had simple and clear missions, or tried to lure gamers with challenging fights or cool graphics, SimCity really had no purpose. It was simply a game of pure creativity. Design a city, however you like. Zone areas for industry or residential or commerce as you see fit. Charge taxes, decide the types of electricity you provide, ensure you have appropriate hospitals and schools and parks, and see how your city grows.

There was a tremendous amount of learning in the game, to be sure. You saw how difficult it was to keep people happy with low taxes yet still provide the education and fire/police protection that they desired. You saw the difficult trade-off decisions politicians face: do we spend more for clean energy, or provide a booming economy with cheaper, dirtier energy? You saw the impact of power plants and crime rates on housing.

It was a brilliantly fun game. For a geek like me, SimCity was amazing. It was like a huge experimental world to build.

After my time in that class, I went out and bought SimCity. And then SimCity 2000. And then SimCity 3000. And then SimCity 4. And SimTower. And SimEarth. Then I got married and got a job, and my bride made it clear that I had an actual real-life world to build. So my time playing SimCity slowly faded away.

But in the meantime, I must have created thousands of cities, some quite intricate. It was a great challenge. Could I create a thriving city on top of a ridiculously rocky mountain range? Could I create a city spread across multiple islands? Could I create a truly pollution-free city, free from roads and surviving only on public transportation and green energy? Could I create a city with a perfect road grid and thus eliminate all traffic jams right from the beginning?

Interestingly, all of those cities ended the same way. In SimCity you had to be able to handle natural disasters: tornadoes, flooding, fires, earthquakes, etc. Before long, though, I found out that there were cheat codes which would allow you to send such disasters at your command. Remember what I said in the last chapter about the uses of the Law? Well, as soon as I knew that I had the power to do the wrong thing and destroy my carefully-built city, you can imagine what happened. (Before you hire me as a city planner or government official, I feel obligated to disclose that a disproportionately high percentage of cities I have built were destroyed by aliens and natural disasters. I'm sure one day a psychologist will find this to be an early warning sign of something.)

Even though I put hours and hours of my life into building these cities, and even though I truly did care about all of that work (I would have been furious, for example, if someone deleted one on which I was still working), ultimately it was just a game. The Sim citizens were not real people, not people like me or my friends. I didn't actually care what happened to them. They had a rudimentary form of artificial intelligence, but they were not real in the way I was real, and so they were just bits and bytes in the computer. I had created them and could delete them, and I could create others. They meant nothing to me personally. They are just *Sims*, after all.

+ + + theology: theological anthropology + + +

In chapter two, we discussed the Creation by the great Engineer, culminating in the creation of man. Then in chapter three, we saw the fall of man, and the beginning of our spiritual gravitational collapse. But as of yet, we have not really talked much about these men that God created. This is the study that theologians call *theological anthropology*, the study of man in relation to God.

Often when I think of theological anthropology, I think back to my time as creator of all of those Sim cities. The only investment I felt for those little Sims who went from home to work and complained to me about tax rates was that I had spent time creating them. In and of themselves, they held no value for me; they were valuable only insofar as they served as vessels of my energy in creating them. As soon as the interest they gave me was less than the energy it would take to continue to play, I would wipe them out in flood or fire or tornado or file deletion.

And yet, this is not how God apparently sees us. When the Bible speaks of man, it is in bold, shocking terms. We are made in the "image" or likeness of God (Gen 1:26). He names us His regent to rule over the Earth, with authority over the animals and plants (Gen 1: 26, 28-30). He tells us to be fruitful and fill and own the earth (Gen 1:29). He blesses only man, and no other creation (Gen 1:28). He breathes a soul of life into Adam (Gen 2:7), and makes for him a reproductive partner (Gen 2:22-24). And, as we see throughout Scripture, the one constant throughout history has been God's consistent forgiveness of man's rebelliousness. He is pictured in Scripture using a variety of metaphors: a husband faithful despite his wife's infidelity, a loving father despite his son's rebellion, a generous master despite his worker's inadequacies. We are told, in fact, that God loves us with *agape* love: a sacrificial, unconditional love.

This has always shocked me. I do not understand, nor will I ever, how God could care so much about mankind. I can relate to how pagans inventing religions could invent distant gods or mean-spirited gods or gods who simply do not care much about us. I cannot really relate to a God who creates us and, despite the wealth of distance between Him and us, loves us with an unstopping love.

I could never have that feeling about my Sims. Even if somehow I could give them true life, I still cannot ever imagine a scenario in which I would love them in the same way that I love my sons. After all, roaches and ants are living things, but I give no thought to stepping on one if I find it in my kitchen. So I doubt that simply the fact that they were alive would make me care about them, and certainly not in a familial way.

And yet, this is exactly what the Bible says God does. He loves us in unconditional ways, so much so that He is willing to give His own Son to bring us back into right relationship with Him (John 3:16).

While theological anthropology does not fully answer how God can be so full of love, it does help us to understand a bit about these Sims He created and into whom He breathed life. In particular, theological anthropology explores the nature of man, what it means to be the "image of God," and what happens after death.

The Nature of Man

The primary question of theological anthropology is to understand the nature of man. In other words, we know we have a physical, three-dimensional body; we know we are capable of rational thought through our brains; and we know from Scripture that we have something called a spirit or soul. How do these interact with one another to form a human being?

The body (in Greek, *soma*) is the physical aspect of the human being. It is a three-dimensional spatial body which is subject to the laws of nature. It contains the brain and other organs, and is essentially materialistic in its nature. So think of it like a more advanced version of your Sim: the body is the physical form and space occupied by the Sim, including its intelligence (AI) and instincts.

The soul (*nepes*) is generally seen throughout Christian history as something lacking in physical size (at least in our three dimensions), yet which is somehow connected to us. It is noteworthy that all cultures of all religious traditions have said something similar: we all feel our spirit and we know it is here and a part of us; indeed, most throughout history have said it is the most real part of us. But we cannot see it or measure it or weigh it. It is something which has historically been viewed as immortal and spiritual (that is, immaterial).

How these two interact is generally explained using one of two theologies: *dichotomism* or *monism*.

Dichotomism is the traditional Christian view, saying that the human being is the melding of two components: a body/flesh, and a soul/spirit. Upon death, the link between the two is severed, and the soul is freed from the fleshly body; they will be rejoined when, at the end of time, the body is resurrected and made whole again. If we think of our Sims as living on our computer monitor (a Flatland), then the soul is something like a balloon in our Spaceland which is connected to their Flatland counterparts; when they are dead (erased from the screen), the balloon remains floating in Spaceland and is now untethered from the body of the Sim.

Monism is a much more rare view, but has some popularity among modern theologians. The monists argue that the body/soul duality comes from a Greek understanding and instead think it is more consistent to view the body and soul not as separate components but rather as two parts of one whole.

The Image of God

When the Bible says we are made in the 'image of God', it does not mean that God has a corporeal body which resembles humans (with two eyes, a mouth, a waistline that continually expands, etc.). There really is not a firm agreement in Christian theology on exactly what this means, but as Millard J. Erickson notes, the phrase "image of God" is generally understood in one of three ways: the *Substantive*, *Relational*, or *Functional* view.

The **substantive** view states that we are said to be "in the image of God" because we have some characteristic which is like God. Most commonly this is said to be the spiritual nature of man. Others argue it is our capacity to exert willpower (rather than simply follow our instincts like the animals), or our ability to reason and have abstract thought. So the substantivist says that when God created in His image, it would be like us creating a two-dimensional Sim and attaching a third-dimensional component to him: we are making him like us in a fundamental, "essence" way.

Some theologians, like Karl Barth, hold the **relational** view, which states that it is the ability to form spiritual relationships which makes us like God. God as a Trinity is inherently defined by an unbreakable spiritual relationship between three Persons; this view argues that the same is true of humans. Since other creatures have no such ability, this is our "image" of God. So to use our Sims analogy, this would be like saying that if I gave my Sims the ability to form relationships with each other, then I have made them in my image.

Others argue the **functional** view, which states that our "God's image" is the functional role that God gave us as His regents over the Earth. We are "in God's image" in that we are His rulers on Earth, just as He is ruler over the Universe and us. So this would be like saying to my Sims, "I give you these jobs, and thus you are in my image, for just as I have the job of ruling your City, you have the job of acting as my stewards."

Frankly, I have never seen these as mutually exclusive positions. It seems to me all three cases constitute a difference between man and the other creations God made, and thus are part of us having been made in the "image of God."

When we die

Another key topic of theological anthropology is the study of what happens when we die. As we saw in chapter three, the Fall of Man brought about death. No longer were we in perfect harmony with God, but now our own gravity was causing us to collapse and implode upon ourselves spiritually, only being sustained through God's grace.

Christianity has always taught that there is an afterlife, for even though the body has a limitation on age, the soul does not. The Bible and Christian theology teach that when our physical body dies, the soul becomes separated from it. The two will remain separated until the end of time; then, the body will be resurrected and rejoined to the soul. In later chapters we will discuss what happens next: either the New Life (in which the consequences from the Fall are set back right) or the Second Death.

But of interest to theological anthropology is the question of what happens *before* the final judgment but *after* the death of the body: the *intermediate state* of the soul. To use our Sim analogy, let us say that our Sim has died on the screen, but his balloon-like soul is still floating around in my house, even though his body no longer exists in the computer. What happens then?

There have been, broadly, three views of what happens when the soul is separated from the body, which I call: the *Grave*, *Paradise Previewed*, and *Purgatory*.

The traditional Christian view, which I call the **Grave** view, was the one held by most Jews at the time Jesus lived. This view stated that after death the soul existed in an intermediate place called *sheol* in Hebrew or *hades* in Greek. It was seen as consisting of two sections, one for the righteous and one for the unrighteous. There the souls waited until the resurrection of the bodies. In 1 Peter 3:18-19, we are told that during the three days of Jesus' death, He was in *hades* preaching to the souls who were there waiting for final judgment. This seems to be the most common view of the early church fathers, and is easily seen directly in Scripture (Gen 37:35, Gen 42:38, Gen 44:29-31, Deut 32:22, 1 Sam 2:6, 1 Kin 2:6-9, Job 7:9, Pro 9:18, Matt 16:18, Luke 16:23, Acts 2:27, Rev 20:13-14).

The second view, which I call the **Paradise Previewed** view, is held by more modern Christians, and uses as evidence passages like Luke 23:43. It says that the souls of the dead immediately are in either Heaven (God's kingdom) or Hell (the lake of fire of Rev 20:13-14) upon their death, though they are not yet re-united to their bodies. The souls remain in these locations as a preview of their eternal fates; then, at the end of time the bodies are resurrected and reunited to them, and they depart to their eternal resting places (New Life or Second Death).

The third view is one held only by Catholics and Anglicans and a few Wesleyans. This view is called **Purgatory**. In this view, after death the souls of Christians experience Purgatory, a process of purification which makes the soul ready for heaven. To use our analogy from chapter three, this would be a place where the *spiritual gravity* was broken off of a person, so that only the *spiritual force* of God's grace remained. Technically speaking the Catholics have never said that purgatory is an actual place, but rather is a process of purification; this could in theory be happening in the same *sheol/hades* that was discussed in the traditional Grave view. While in this process of purgatory, souls are purified and achieve the grace necessary to ascend into heaven; this remaining amount of punishment and purification can be eased for your loved ones by praying for the dead or the church granting "indulgences"—a forgiveness of sins which should have been purified in purgatory but instead are ignored. It was the practice of selling such indulgences for money which so angered Martin Luther and sparked the Protestant Reformation.

We will discuss what happens after death more detail in chapters 16 and 17. For now, let us discuss each of these stances using our Sims analogy. Let's say that for each Sim, I truly love them and give them (somehow) a balloon soul which is attached to them. This soul exists only in my world (Spaceland) and they cannot see it in Flatland; yet still they know somehow that it is there. When they die in the game, their souls continue to exist in Spaceland even though the Flatland body is dead. Eventually I am going to re-create a new game, and give them all new bodies and re-attach their souls. But until that point, their souls are untethered to their bodies, floating around my house like, well, so many balloons. So what happens to them?

The *Grave* view says that I gather anyone's soul that has died and put them all in a room (let's say the laundry room). I put the good ones over by the washer and the bad ones over by the dryer. There they float until I re-create the game later.

The *Paradise Previewed* view says that I put the balloons in their eventual eternal destination so that they can experience a preview before the body is re-created. Thus I leave the good balloons in my room watching as I continue to play the game with the living Sims; the bad balloons I throw outside into the backyard so that they can see what awaits them later.

The *Purgatory* view says that none (or very few) of the balloons are good enough to get into my room yet and watch me play. So most of them stay in the laundry room, shaking off the bad things they did as Sims until they can rejoin me.

Notice that the key thing which is amazing to me remains unanswered and mysterious: why does God love us so? The difference between God and me is much greater than the difference between me and a Sims character. God is powerful enough and intelligent enough to invent out of His mind everything around us, and yet He cares (immensely) how everyone is living in this Spaceland, and whether their souls are in the condition He desires for His eternal plans. It is really fascinating to me, and mysterious. This grace, this love, is truly amazing.

Ironically, though I may be awed in wonder about God's powerful love because of a kid's game, it is a kid's Bible which, I believe, best describes this love. The *Jesus Storybook Bible* calls God's love for man, "a Never Stopping, Never Giving Up, Unbreaking, Always and Forever Love."

I may not know why He has this love for we Sims, especially given our Fall and rebellious natures; but thank God He does.

– SIX –

SPECIFICATIONS

Interestingly, one of the most critical aspects of engineering is something which was not covered in a single course I took in school. I only learned the importance of properly writing engineering specifications when I was in the workforce; from what I have seen, this is true of other engineers as well.

Engineering specifications are explicit sets of requirements that a material or product must satisfy in order to be certain that performance will be acceptable. Failure to meet even one of the specifications may result in the product being unusable.

My first apprenticeship in engineering was working for a metallurgical quality laboratory at a fastener plant. We made structural bolts and nuts which were used in automotive and construction projects, so needless to say we took our quality responsibilities quite seriously. Failure to properly specify our materials or meet the tolerances of our parts could result in a bridge collapse, car accident, or farm disaster.

Part of my job was to work on the team which ensured our bolts and nuts met quality control standards. We would sample parts off of the line and compare them to the engineering specifications for the product. If they were within specification they could go to the customer; if out of specification the parts either had to be reworked or scrapped.

Throughout this and my later jobs, I saw many examples of failures which occurred due to poor specification-writing by the engineers. This is a big deal. If, as the engineer, you did not specify a particular dimension or tolerance or material type, then often the part would fail in the field as a result of your error. Generally speaking, production processes and suppliers do not ask questions: if you do not specify it, then they assume it is up to them to choose the detail in question. So it is critical that the engineer very specifically notes exactly what his design assumptions were in the engineering specification.

It is also critical that the engineering specification be reasonable. Often I have seen engineers specify tolerances which production could not meet. Such a mistake has led to several key engineering failures throughout history, including the collapse of the Kansas City Hyatt Regency walkway in 1981. The Hyatt disaster killed 114 people and injured 216 others, remaining the deadliest structural collapse in American history until September 11. The root cause of the Hyatt disaster was that the specifications made by the engineer were not achievable in practicality; thus the contractor (without consulting the engineer) re-designed the walkway during installation. The contractors of course were not engineers, and as such they did not realize how their redesign would improperly transfer the loading. Their changes resulted in the beams only being able to hold 30% of the minimum required load. The deadly collapse was inevitable after these alterations, due to a failure of the engineer to make reasonable specifications, and the failure of the contractor to follow them.

Over my relatively short career (I am not *that* old, despite what my kids think) I have seen dozens of types of engineering specifications, and many times I cannot help but notice the key missing information. Eventually I noticed that all good specifications fit a certain form: they all had unique identifiers, including revision levels; they listed all requirements for raw materials; they listed all appropriate tolerances; they listed any applicable national standards; they specified any related drawings; etc.

Failure to have any one of these pieces of information could result in structural failure of the part. The simple (and scary) fact is that rarely does a structure fail which was simply designed with too little safety margin. Generally, structural failure happens because the engineer doing the designing does not properly communicate his specifications and assumptions to the people making, installing, or using the item—or he does communicate them well, and the people using the specifications simply ignore them.

A proper specification, then, is critical. Without proper specification one cannot tell whether or not the parts are performing as designed, and whether they will be successful or are destined for structural failure and collapse.

+ + + theology: suzerain covenants and the Law + + +

In the Ancient Near East (aka, "Bible times"), a sacred agreement between two parties was called a covenant. Covenants were common; in fact, covenants were so common that you might well describe the entire Bible as little more than a series of covenants between God and man.

In historical terms, we call the covenants of Biblical times *suzerain covenants*. A suzerain covenant is a covenant where one party is a powerful entity and the other party is a vassal. In Israel's history, for example, they underwent periods of being vassals to a variety of greater powers, such as the Hittites, Egyptians, and Assyrians.

Just like engineering specifications, these suzerain covenants were written in a very specific form, making sure to identify all necessary aspects in order to ensure the treaty would be upheld for years to come. Regardless of the culture, the form of these treaties (which started when the Hittites were in power) generally follows the same basic pattern:

Preamble: identifying the parties involved in the treaty

Prologue: listing the historical interaction between the parties, focusing on the actions performed by the suzerain party on behalf of the vassal

Conditions and Terms: a list of stipulations to which the vassal agrees

Deposition of the Covenant: a presentation of the covenant to the vassal, either through a physical copy or a public reading

Witnesses of the Covenant: a list of witnesses who could validate the covenant (in most polytheistic cultures these were other gods; in Judaism's case, these were generally objects or people)

Curses and blessings: description of the punishments for breaking the covenant or blessings for following the covenant.

This form is seen time and time again throughout the history of the ancient Near East, and the Bible is actually full of such covenants, though often Christians fail to realize it. Throughout the Old Testament we see God enact a series of suzerain covenants with men, and the history and prophetic literature demonstrates for us the success or failure of Israel to uphold the covenants.

For example, let us consider the covenant between God and Noah (the "Noahic Covenant") in Genesis 7:1-9:17. The suzerain party is God the Father; the vassals are Noah and his descendants (including us!); the broker or mediator of the covenant is Noah. So even though you may not have realized it, the story of Noah actually is a by-the-book suzerain treaty of the ancient Near East.

The *Preamble* is Genesis 9:8-11, where God enacts a covenant with Noah and his descendents.

The *Prologue* is Gen 6:1-8:20, in which we see man being evil on the earth, and God wiping out the earth through the Flood but sparing Noah. This section is often just read as history and thus its role in the Noahic Covenant is missed. Notice how little time God spends telling about the evil people who needed to be wiped out: a mere 8 verses, compared to 61 verses describing how God took care of Noah and his family. This section is not merely to recount history, but to serve as the historical prologue establishing why God had the rights as a suzerain over Noah and his family.

The *Conditions and Terms* are in Gen 9:1-7, where man is commanded to do four things: (1) be fruitful and multiply (continuing God's covenant with Adam, of whom Noah is a descendant); (2) not eating the blood of animals; (3) not to commit murder; and (4) to execute murderers.

The *Deposition of the Covenant* is done by God speaking directly to Noah in Gen 9:1-7.

As *Witness*, God takes the rainbow (which already existed) and re-purposes it as an evidence of the covenant (Gen 9:12-17). God did not create the rainbow at this time. (For as long as the sky existed and the clouds gave rain, there have been rainbows! Otherwise, the physical laws of the entire universe would have had to be completely different prior to this point and created anew during this passage.) But He took this existing feature of the sky and gave it sacred meaning, saying that every time we see a rainbow it can serve as a witness of the covenant God made with Noah.

For *Blessings and Cursings*, God promises (as a blessing) He will never again wipe out the earth. Further, God says that if one of Noah's descendents is found to be in violation of this covenant (such as by killing another man), his life shall be forfeit and he should be executed.

This is just one of many examples illustrating how Israel, being an Ancient Near Eastern culture, organized its covenants with God in the standard manner of their day. Failing to understand this may result in misreading the Scriptures.

But when people talk about "The Law," or the "Old Covenant," they are not talking about God's covenant with Adam, or with Noah, or with Abraham, or with David. (God made a lot of covenants with mankind; we kept screwing it up.)

The primary Biblical covenant between God and man took place at Mount Sinai. You all, I am certain, remember the Sunday School lessons of Moses leading the captive Israelites out of Egypt and into the Promised Land. Or, if not a fan of Sunday School, you probably have seen one of the many showings of Charlton Heston's *Ten Commandments* every Easter season. Or that cartoon version where Val Kilmer plays Moses. (To all you younger geeks: for about fifteen minutes, Val Kilmer was the geek hero of movies. He played the main character in *The Island of Doctor Moreau*, based upon a great sci-fi book; he was the coolest Batman of the 90's Batman movies; and he played an awesome assassin in *The Saint*. You cannot imagine how cool he was to us geeks back in the day.)

Anyway, Moses lived a long time ago; Christians generally date Moses' life as being around 1500 BC, while Jewish rabbinical sources place his life around 1300 BC. Moses, being the *de facto* leader of the now-freed Jews, was led by God to Mount Sinai.

On Sinai, Moses and God enact a covenant. This is the "big" covenant of the Old Testament. It tells the Jews how to live in order to please God, receive His blessing on their lives, and gain His protection for their nation.

In engineering terms, this is God's statement of His **specifications**. These are the rules by which we as His material creations are expected to abide. It is His depiction of how a well-functioning version of His designed humans would act, and He chose the Jews as a sort of "sample size" of humanity to attempt to uphold this Law.

(Note: the book of Exodus records the initial events around the Mosaic Covenant, and the book of Deuteronomy is simply a second telling of the same Law. So I will cite both the Exodus and Deuteronomy references herein.)

Preamble

"Moses went up to God, and the Lord called to him from the mountain, saying, 'Thus shall you say to the house of Jacob and tell the sons of Israel.' " (Exo 19:3; Deut 1:1-4).

So the parties are identified, with God serving as the suzerain and the sons of Israel (the Jewish people, the "chosen ones") as the vassals. Moses, as the liberator, spokesman, prophet, and prime minister of the Israelites, serves as the Mediator of the covenant.

Historical Prologue

"You yourselves have seen what I did to the Egyptians, and how I bore you on eagles' wings, and brought you to Myself.

Now then, if you will indeed obey My voice and keep My covenant, then you shall be My own possession among all the people, for all the earth is Mine; and you shall be to Me a kingdom of priests and a holy nation." (Exo 19:4-6; Deut 1:5-4:43)

In the historical prologue, God reminds His people why He has the right of being a suzerain: without Him, they would never have been freed from bondage in Egypt.

Conditions and Terms

"Then God spoke all these words, saying, 'I am the LORD your God, who brought you out of the land of Egypt, out of the house of slavery. You shall have no other gods before Me. You shall not make for yourself an idol, or any likeness of what is in heaven above or on the earth beneath or in the water under the earth. You shall not worship them or serve them; for I, the LORD your God, am a jealous God, visiting the iniquity of the fathers on the children, on the third and the fourth generations of those who hate Me, but showing lovingkindness to thousands, to those who love Me and keep My commandments.

You shall not take the name of the LORD your God in vain, for the LORD will not leave him unpunished who takes His name in vain. Remember the sabbath day, to keep it holy. Six days you shall labor and do all your work, but the seventh day is a sabbath of the LORD your God; in it you shall not do any work, you or your son or your daughter, your male or your female servant or your cattle or your sojourner who stays with you. For in six days the LORD made the heavens and the earth, the sea and all that is in them, and rested on the seventh day; therefore the LORD blessed the sabbath day and made it holy.

Honor your father and your mother, that your days may be prolonged in the land which the LORD your God gives you. You shall not murder. You shall not commit adultery. You shall not steal. You shall not bear false witness against your neighbor. You shall not covet your neighbor's house; you shall not covet your neighbor's wife or his male servant or his female servant or his ox or his donkey or anything that belongs to your neighbor.' " (Exo 20:1-17; Deut 4:44-26:19)

The book of Deuteronomy expands on these basic Ten Commandments in much more detail. From the passages of Exodus, Leviticus, and Deuteronomy, the Jews known as the Pharisees derived 613 commandments of God.

Six hundred and thirteen! This is an overwhelming list of commandments. You had to be a legal expert and study your entire life just to be able to learn them all, and following them was seemingly impossible. Recall that in chapter three, we discussed the natural spiritual gravitation of man. This covenant shows us the strength of the gravitational force of our spirits: no person is even close to being able to avoid failing to at least some of these 613 commandments. Spiritual collapse, under such a law, is a certainty.

Witnesses to the Covenant

Between Exodus 19:7-8, Exodus 24:8-12, and Deuteronomy 27:1-10, three primary forms of witnesses of the covenant were created.

The first witness was a stone tablet, written by God Himself, which listed the Ten Commandments (the basics of the Law). These were placed within the Ark of the Covenant to be kept by Israel forever. (Spoiler alert: They lost it. Typical contractors, losing the engineering specs halfway through the job.)

Second was the universal acceptance of the covenant by its people, as demonstrated by a public sprinkling of blood on the people.

Third was the institution of the Feast of Passover, an annual celebration to remember God saving His people from Egypt.

Even though the transcripts were written in stone they were lost. Before long, the public sprinkling was forgotten. The only thing which was never lost was the annual party.

These three things together were the witnesses of the Law.

Cursings and Blessings

> "Now then, if you will indeed obey My voice and keep My covenant, then you shall be My own possession among all the peoples, for all the earth is Mine; and you shall be to Me a kingdom of priests and a holy nation." (Exo 19:5-6; Deut 27:11-30:20)

With this covenant, God established for mankind exactly what His specifications would require. They were tough, but He spelled them out clearly, and chose the Israelites as a sort of "sample size" of the total population: a special group who would be tested to see if they could maintain their commitment to the specifications given to them by the Great Engineer.

But as we mentioned in chapter three, spiritual gravity made success impossible. The entire Old Testament after Deuteronomy records one instance after another of the Jews failing, despite incredible effort and willpower, to uphold the covenant of God. For some centuries they completely ignored and forgot the Law altogether; for others they tried desperately to uphold it. But never for more than the shortest periods of time did God's people manage to achieve their requirements under the covenant.

Any good engineer knows what happens when you get materials which do not conform to specifications. You can choose to rework or scrap the bad parts. In the Flood, prior to Noah, God chose to scrap them; but after the Noahic Covenant, God agreed to never do so again. So it seems that rework was the only option available to Him: providing some physical action which brings the bad product back into specification.

God did indeed put Israel through many periods of rework. They were forced to wander in the desert for a generation at one point. They were conquered by the Assyrians, the Persians, the Babylonians, and the Romans at various points in their history; each time, according to the Bible, was because of their rebellion against the Law and was intended to bring them back to God's covenant. In other words, these were all painful periods of God reworking non-conforming materials.

But there were simply too many reworks. Eventually God gave up on trying to rework and rework and rework the nation of Israel. They were never going to meet specifications, and that fact is now clear not only to God, but to the Israelites as well. Thus, the Law served two primary purposes: first, to show men the specifications that they were supposed to uphold; and second, to demonstrate that such specifications were impossible to maintain, due to the spiritual gravity experienced by all men.

– SEVEN –

THE GREAT COMPOSITE

As discussed earlier, the geek in me was naturally drawn to the field of engineering. It was a natural fit: a little bit of math, a lot of science, and a ton of technology...frankly it was a bit hard to believe that they would pay me to do it. Although the Internet was still just emerging as a major source of information (good grief, that makes me feel old), I spent a lot of hours online and reading books and magazines about how things were made. The day that Popular Mechanics arrived was the highlight of each month. I just always knew I wanted to invent things for a living. I wanted to take what I knew about science and turn it into something to make the world a better place to live. (Or at least, to make the world "not worse" while bringing in good money.)

Knowing I wanted to be an engineer, I frequently talked with my grandfather (who was CEO of a local company, and employed several engineers) about how to prepare for my career. His advice was always the same: study hard, but even more importantly, get great experience as young as possible. It was the experience, he argued, that set apart the good engineers from the great ones. So from the time I was 17, I spent every summer and winter working engineering internships: two terms at a fastener company which extruded metal wire to manufacture nuts and bolts; two terms at an electronics manufacturer which used stamped metal pins and injection-molded casings to make electrical connectors for phones and computers; and then two terms at an automotive company, using metal to manufacture school buses.

As you might imagine from this list of experiences, when I graduated, I felt most comfortable in the worlds of metalworking and forming. So for my first real engineering job, I joined the oldest continually-operating manufacturer in North America, Remington Arms Company. At Remington we used metalworking techniques such as stamping, drawing, and heat treating to form ammunition casings and bullets, and then using semi-automated equipment we combined them together to form working rounds of ammunition.

At Remington, I spent nearly six years under a great Christian engineer named Keith, where I learned lessons applicable both to my spiritual life and my professional life. Though I enjoyed and grew during those years, eventually I just did not feel professionally challenged. As you might imagine, for a company which had been making the same products since before the Civil War (on equipment which was often from the World War I era), overhauling the processes was not seen as an urgent need. In addition, metalworking had grown a bit dull for me. The engineering principles were simple, and most days I felt like a mechanic with a degree, rather than an innovator.

So when I got a call from a major composites company moving into the area, I thought getting in at the ground floor of a fast-growing company sounded like a lot of fun. Of course, I knew next to nothing about composites, but I figured, "What the heck? I'm a smart guy, I'll pick it up quickly."

Wow, was I in for a surprise.

It turns out composites are much more difficult to work with than metals. The manufacturing I had been used to, where you have alloys of metal and you perform various highly-controlled heating, forming, and cooling actions on them, is really pretty straightforward. That is not the case with composites; they are very unpredictable.

Composites are engineered materials formed from multiple other materials, each of which has different physical or chemical properties. The combination of these materials creates a new material (the composite) which gains the benefits of each of these sub-materials. Everything from concrete to your bathtub to straw-and-mud huts are examples of composite materials.

For example, at our company we produce a composite wind turbine blade. Without delving into any proprietary information, what we do is arrange several tons of fiberglass material in a particular pattern based upon our customer's requirements; we then inject the fibers with a polyester resin which has been pre-mixed with a peroxide hardener.

The liquid chemical mixture of polyester and peroxide travels throughout the tons of fiberglass in a process we call infusion. During infusion, the individual glass fibers become completely saturated with the resin. Meanwhile, inside the resin the hardener produces free radicals, which bounce around in the chemical concoction and open double bonds in the polyester chains to allow for bonding.

After enough bonds are opened, the polyester chains begin to bond to each other. They release heat in the process, which further weakens the surrounding bonds. This makes the next bond easier to break, and thus the bonding continues exponentially. Eventually, after sufficient curing time, we end up with a new composite product, called a "laminate." This laminate functions as a wind turbine blade.

This wind turbine blade is an infused fiber-reinforced composite. It has the properties of both the polyester resin and of the glass fibers, but the two are now one material, chemically bonded together by the working of the hardener. The composite material is made of two unique materials with their own properties (fiberglass and polyester resin), and sustained because of bonding created by a third material (peroxide hardener).

What is most interesting about a composite is its nature of being both "one" and "many," simultaneously. If we go up to one of our blades and try to separate the resin from the fiber, we will find it impossible to do so without destroying the laminate completely. The resin is bonded permanently to the fiber, and cannot be separated without the destruction of both; indeed, when this happens it is called a "delamination" and is considered a serious failure which must be repaired.

You see, the fibers have their own unique properties and are their own unique material, just as the resin has its own properties and is its own unique material, and the hardener has its own properties and is its own unique material. Individually they are useless to the wind energy industry. They are only valuable as parts of a new "one"—combined together, they bond inseparably to create a new object which never before existed, and cannot exist separate from the component materials within.

+ + + theology: the hypostatic union + + +

Recall in our last chapter, we saw the agreed-upon specifications for mankind as dictated by God. We have also seen that mankind was incapable of living up to the Law, and much of the Old Testament was dedicated to recounting the ways in which the Jews had failed to live up to their promises.

The New Testament, however, is based upon the life and teachings of one particular Jew, Jesus of Nazareth. This man was a lightning rod for criticism during His life. To the outsider He was a carpenter's son from the most bumpkin area (Nazareth) of the most backwater province (Judea) in the Empire. He was viewed with the same kind of revulsion that you or I have for the weirdoes on *Swamp People*. Not only was Jesus a nobody, but there were some rumors that His teenage mother might have been pregnant before she was married. Nobody knew for sure, because her fiancé took off after the census and they lived in another country for a while, where no one could be completely sure of the boy's birth date. Any way you look at it, clearly He was a simple, humble, unassuming Jew—nothing special. There were millions just like Him. Or so it seemed, for a while.

Then one day, this Jesus starts doing all manner of miracles and teaching all kinds of bold things, the boldest of which are the times when He equated Himself to God. Some skeptics try to claim that Jesus never actually claimed to be God, but it is clear in the Scripture that Jesus made exactly such an incredible claim about His divine nature. In Matthew 23:29-36, Jesus claims to be the One who sent the prophets and curses the Pharisees for their hypocrisy. In Matthew 26:63-65 and Luke 22:67-70, Jesus agreed that He had indeed claimed Godhood. In Mark 2:1-12, Jesus claims God's right as the only person allowed to forgive sins. In Mark 14:60-62, He plainly claims to be the Messiah and the son of God. In John 4 and 5, Jesus claims to be the living water which can bring eternal salvation, and claims God's right to do work on the Sabbath. In John 8:24, Jesus identifies Himself again as God (using the phrase 'I AM', which was used by God when talking to Moses back in Exodus), and says that belief in Him is the only path to heaven. In John 10:11-18, Jesus identifies Himself as the good Shepherd responsible for Israel. In John 10:33, Jesus' enemies threaten to stone Him for claiming to be God (which would be a strange thing to try and do if He was not claiming divinity).

In the next chapter, we will see how Jesus' life ties into the failure of man to uphold their engineering specifications. But first, let us go into one of the most divisive debates in the early Christian church: who exactly was this man who changed the course of history? As we see above He clearly claimed to be God in the flesh, but at other times we are told that He was tempted like a man (Matt 4), was born of a woman (Luke 2, Matt 2), was raised and grew up as a human child (Luke 2:39-52), and therefore clearly He seems to be a real human. Which was it: was He God or man?

Some have argued that Jesus was just a man, with no divinity in Him. The "just a man" theories come in many varieties. Some say He was a lunatic with the original "Messianic" complex, and that (as lunatics sometimes do) He gathered a following. Others say He was just a great moral teacher and His execution was not (as the Gospels claim) for the blasphemy of claiming divinity, but rather for challenging the current beliefs of his time. Still others say He was a liar or possessed by the devil; indeed, this is exactly what He was accused of in John 8. The Muslims claim He was a prophet, but deny He was anything more.

On the other side, some throughout history have argued that Jesus was purely God. He was not tempted as men are tempted; He could not have sinned; He did not feel what we feel. He was purely God appearing to us in a way we could see. He was never "stained" by the things of this world. This was particularly popular among those of Greek philosophical descent, since many Greeks saw the material world as evil and the spiritual world as pure; so Jesus had to be one or the other, and many said He was just purely a spiritual being.

Both of these views were roundly rejected as heresy by the early church, and cannot be supported with the writings of the apostles in the New Testament. Rather, the early Christian theologians in their attempts to describe Jesus ended up with a theology called the *hypostatic union*. The word hypostatic was first used by the bishop Apollinarius of Laodicea (? – 390). He said that when Jesus was born of the virgin Mary, the divine nature of God and the human nature of Jesus were a single essence, completely inseparable. Jesus was not God wearing a human mask; He was not God only; He was not man only. He was simultaneously God and man, and the two natures were inseparable within Him. When the topic was debated by the Christian theologians at the Council of Chalcedon, it was agreed that Jesus was made of two separate and distinct natures—human and divine—but that the two were united together into one concrete substance in the person of Christ.

This has long been a topic of great confusion among Christians. How are we to understand the concept of a hypostatic union? How can Jesus be both God and man at the same time?

For composites engineers, such a definition is perhaps easier to understand than for some others. In our wind turbine blades, recall that the polyester resin and fiberglass each retain their own properties at all times. The resin does not cease to be resin after bonding; nor does the fiberglass cease to be fiberglass after being saturated. The two materials maintain their own unique properties.

Yet, when bonded together through the activity of the hardener, the two cease to be separable and instead become a completely new substance – a material which has the properties of both simultaneously, and is a new thing entirely. It ceases to be several tons of fiberglass and polyester; it is now a wind turbine blade, something altogether new and yet still containing the individual natures of the materials of which it is comprised. The polyester and fibers are different things with their own properties, but are bonded together in a union which cannot be separated and which creates something totally new.

This is true of any composite. In mud-and-straw huts, the straw retains its properties and the mud retains its properties and together they are something with new properties, even while each retain their uniqueness. In concrete footings, the concrete retains its properties and the rebar retains its properties, and together they now have new properties which did not previously exist. They are *inseparable* but still retain their *uniqueness.*

The nature of Jesus is not significantly different.

In the Gospel of John, we are told that the *logos*, or divine Word of God, took human form in the event theologians call the Incarnation:

"In the beginning was the Word, and the Word was with God, and the Word was God. ...And the Word became flesh and dwelt among us, and we have seen His glory, glory as of the only Son from the Father, full of grace and truth." (John 1:1,14, ESV)

So how did this occur? The Bible records only what Mary was told by the angel Gabriel:

"And behold, you will conceive in your womb and bear a son, and you shall call His name Jesus...The Holy Spirit will come upon you, and the power of the Most High will overshadow you; therefore the child to be born will be called holy—The Son of God." (Luke 1:31,35, ESV)

From the Scriptures we can confidently conclude a few facts regarding this event.

First, we see that it is truly God, the Creator Himself (John 1:1-3), who became flesh (v.14). Jesus pre-existed creation and indeed was of one substance with the Father throughout the acts of creation. This is the divine spirit of God and thus the child is called the Son of God (Lk 1:35). So we must reject the concept that Jesus was not God.

Second, we see that the child is clearly human. Jesus comes from the womb (and egg) of Mary (Lk 1:31). He is truly Mary's son, and it is in response to her faithfulness that she is chosen to bear the Son of God in her womb. So we must reject the concept that Jesus was not Man.

Third, we see that the "bonding agent" is the third member of the Trinity, the Holy Spirit. In Luke 1:35, we see that the action of the Word becoming flesh in Mary's womb is achieved when the Holy Spirit overtakes Mary. The word in the Greek is *eperchomai*, which carries the concept of a stronger person overtaking a weaker one; it is the same word used in Acts 1:8 to describe the Holy Spirit overtaking the apostles on the day of Pentecost.

Recall our composite wind turbine blade, where fiberglass and resin remain unique materials yet are bound together by the actions of a hardener, creating a new "thing" while still retaining their individual natures. The same event occurred during the Incarnation. God's Spirit served as the "hardener" in this case, bonding together the divine nature of the Creator of the Universe with the human egg of Mary, a humble and faithful but generally un-noteworthy woman of first century Judea.

Just as our composite blade still retains the properties of its components, so too does Jesus still retain the properties of both of His natures. He is not only God or only Man: He is something completely new, the God-Man, which never existed before and has never existed since. He is truly at the same moment both fully human and fully God, just as our wind turbine blades are both fully polyester and fully fiberglass. And just as our fiberglass-reinforced composite has new properties because of this relationship, so too does Jesus as God-Man have a new, resultant set of properties.

He maintains the properties of a human, with all of our weakness and physical limitations and temptation for sin and rebellion. And He maintains the properties of God, the all-powerful Creator who was there at the beginning of time. But as with any composite, these two properties combine to create a new, third property: the property of the God-Man, the Word Incarnate.

Jesus became something new, the Great Composite which had never existed before and never will again. He and He alone combines the properties of God and man. And as we shall see, this allows Him to serve in a very unique role in helping us overcome our failures as engineered Men—a role no other individual in history could have served.

– EIGHT –

REINFORCING OUT OF SPEC COMPONENTS

For someone who travels as much as I do, I have a very bad habit of reading with fascination about plane crashes. Perhaps it is the engineer in me, perhaps it is the geek, but I am fascinated to understand the mistakes which engineers made, leading to an otherwise perfectly safe vehicle failing during flight.

The McDonnell Douglas DC-10 is a widebody jet airliner, designed in the 1970s, which was once a major passenger jet and which, despite replacement as a passenger plane in most airlines, still remains in some service today as a cargo plane (with carriers such as FedEx, for example).

The DC-10, however, had a major design flaw which became known just a year after its introduction. In 1972, American Airlines Flight 96 closed the doors and took off from Detroit. The aft cargo door showed that it was properly and securely locked, so everything proceeded normally with the pre-flight inspection and the flight was cleared for takeoff. After takeoff, however, when the crew reached about 12,000 feet, the pressure of the fuselage blew the cargo door completely off of its hinges, collapsing the cabin floor in the rear of the plane; this collapsed floor in turn severed some of the control cables. The pilot was able to heroically land the crippled plane using only partial control systems.

During the investigation, a design flaw was found in the cargo door. Most cargo doors open inward, but this of course reduces the usable space for storing baggage (the area where the door opens must remain clear of bags). So the DC-10 designers had their cargo door open outward, to give more bag storage space. When a plane reaches high altitude, the pressure of the fuselage is very high; for an inward-opening door this is of course no problem, as the pressure of the fuselage merely reinforces that the door remain closed. However, for an outward-opening door, this means that the pressure of the fuselage was constantly providing significant outward force on the door assembly.

To counteract this force, the DC-10 cargo door was designed with heavy locking mechanisms. A set of steel hooks was used to lock onto the door frame. When the hooks were in place, an outside lever would be pulled, sliding locking pins through the hooks to prevent them coming off. This control mechanism was the design flaw, as investigators discovered you could close the outside lever with the pins even if the hooks were not in place. Because the indicator light in the cockpit was triggered by the lever (rather than the hooks *and* the lever), the cockpit would show that the door was properly secured even when it was not.

The FAA made several recommendations to operators of the DC-10, but did not make the change mandatory. Two years later, Turkish Airlines Flight 981 experienced the same incident; this time, however, the collapse of the cabin severed all of the control cables, making the plane impossible to fly. The pilots were helpless, and the plane crashed into a forest in France, killing all 346 passengers. To this day, it remains one of the deadliest airline disasters of all time. Following the crash, the US House of Representatives investigated the issue and the FAA's reaction. After the investigation an airworthiness directive was released, requiring all DC-10 doors to be modified or the planes would be grounded. This corrected the issue going forward.

Sadly for engineers, failure is a certainty in design. What most of the public does not understand is that inventing new products always carries an inherent risk, because the number of potential things which could go wrong is quite high. It is a testament to modern engineers that, despite our massive growth in the past century, we have so few disasters due to design flaws. But as we all know, the Tacoma Bridge and the Kansas City Hyatt Regency walkway and the DC-10s and the Challenger explosion are just a few of many examples where engineers or manufacturers make poor decisions which they believe to be safe, yet failed to account for all possible risks. Failure is unavoidable in engineering, and sometimes the result is the death of innocent bystanders.

As a result, responses to field failures are a major part of the work of engineers on a day-to-day basis. Ethical engineers will not simply ignore known issues (as Morton Thiokol and NASA's managers ignored the known O-ring flaws which downed the Challenger shuttle). Instead, as we discussed in chapter six, when such failures become known, most engineers choose one of two common responses: rework or scrap.

Rework is the process of changing the existing product so that it is no longer capable of experiencing the failure. In cases like the DC-10, replacement of the door with one which could not blow outward would have been exorbitantly expensive, possibly requiring redesign and retesting of the fuselage. As a result they chose rework instead, both attempting to make the door fit more securely and adding ventilation fail-safes so that if the door did get removed for any reason, it would not depressurize the cabin. This rework was effective, and the incidents with the DC-10 did not repeat.

Scrap is sometimes required even for expensive products, but generally is used when the value of the individual components is low. For example, when Toyota became aware of the potential for floor mats to depress the accelerator in 2009, they recalled my Camry and 4Runner, scrapping the old mats and replacing them with thinner mats which hooked into the floorboard. As a result, the mats simply could no longer fail.

However, sometimes there is a third option for handling out-of-specification components: **reinforcement**. In many cases this is inappropriate or ineffective (for example, simply adding more heavy steel hooks on the door of the DC-10 to hold it tighter would have been of little comfort). But often it is the case that a sub-standard product is incapable of carrying its designed load, but can be reinforced with an additional component. This reinforcement reduces the load on the component and allows the entire structure to meet specifications—even though the substandard parts are still substandard.

This is a common approach in the composites industry, where I work. Let us say hypothetically that you have invented a ten-ton wind turbine blade. You begin producing the blade and have no major issues. However, once it is in the field you realize that the bonding lines are too weak; due to some error in design or manufacturing, the bond is unable to support the loads which it is experiencing in the field. Of course, you could go in and remove the bondline and add new bonding, or you could scrap the entire product. But these options are expensive, and thankfully in composites another option exists: reinforcement.

In this case, you send a service crew out to perform what is called in our industry an *over-lamination*: fibers are hand laid up in the weak area and infused with resin to bond it to the substandard area. This new additional composite which was added takes the structural burden off of the failing bondline, instead accepting the additional load itself. As a result, the total structure now functions, even though the failing (non-conforming) parts were never actually improved.

+ + + theology: substitutionary atonement + + +

Let us recall what we have learned so far in our geek's investigation of theology. We learned that God is somehow a Trinity (Father, Son, and Spirit) while remaining a single being. This God was the Great Engineer, who created all of us and everything around us. However, man fails to live up to the specifications God created for us: without His intervention of grace to counteract it, our natural spiritual gravitation (self-centeredness) collapses our spirits until we self-ignite. Time and time again, God tried to fix His non-conforming product. He gave clearer specifications (the Law), but man could not live up to them. He tried rework (for example, the Babylonian captivity), but man did not improve. He even tried the scrap-and-replace method at one point (the Flood), but no matter how God tried to help, as soon as man was left to himself his spiritual gravity caused a collapse into selfishness, sin, and rebellion.

For some reason, even though He is so much greater than us and had done so much for us, God continued to love His rebellious creation. And God had a plan. If scrap-and-replace would not work, and rework was impossible, then God would have to use the third engineering option: to reinforce His people.

And so it was that 2,000 years ago, one member of the Trinity stepped into our three-dimensional world for a period of about 30-40 years. As we saw last chapter, this Jesus was a composite: simultaneously God and man, the one true God incarnate in the flesh. While here, He did many great things: He taught strong morals, He spoke out against hypocrisy, He helped the downtrodden, He healed the sick, He performed miracles. But none of those things, great as they were, were the reason He came to Earth.

Jesus came to be our reinforcement. Just like an overlamination removes the structural load from the failing bondline of a composite, Jesus came to Earth so that the stress and load of the Law could be removed from us. No longer would we be required to adhere to our specifications, because Jesus will take the load off of us and onto Him, and fulfill it perfectly.

This is an act which, in theological terms, we call *substitutionary atonement*. Jesus came and lived a perfect life according to the Law, and died innocently, and somehow His death reconciles us to God. So Jesus (though without sin) dies and this substitution atones for our own sins.

When we overlaminate a composite, notice that the original defective area does not get even slightly stronger: the defect still exists in the product. It is still completely incapable of meeting requirements, and it does not "do" anything or change in any way to make it more acceptable. The only thing which is "done" by the defective area is that it is bonded to the overlaminate. The overlamination does all of the work.

Substitutionary atonement works the same way. When we are saved from our sins, it is not that God removes our sinful nature so that we are inherently acceptable to Him. We are just as defective under the Law as we were before atonement. But Jesus, as the Great Composite, *overlaminates* us: His life "covers" our life as it is, and the load of the Law passes to Him rather than us. Thus when God sees us He does not see our failure before the Law, but rather Jesus' success before the Law covering us. This is why Paul says, in Romans 8:17, that we have become "co-heirs" of Christ: because of Christ's perfect life and His death on the cross, we are viewed as being one with Jesus.

Though substitutionary atonement is a key belief of the faith, there nonetheless has been significant disagreement over the years regarding exactly *how* this atonement works. There are three basic models of substitutionary atonement in Christian theology: the ransom view, the satisfaction view, and the penal substitution view.

The **ransom** view was one of the earliest theologies of atonement, popular in the works of the Christian father Origen. This theory teaches that the Fall of Man sold the souls of mankind over to the devil, and a ransom was needed to "pay off" the debt. God tricks the devil into accepting Jesus as the ransom for death, because the devil was unaware Jesus could not be held by the bounds of the grave. Thus, the death on the cross freed us from our debt, and Jesus' resurrection is the triumph of the plan. This view leans strongly on the literal meaning of the Biblical phrase that Jesus "redeems" us—in the ancient Near East, redeeming meant to buy back someone out of slavery and into freedom. This is also sometimes called the *"Christus Victor"* model of atonement. For the first thousand years or so of Christian history, the ransom theology was the most common explanation for how atonement worked.

The **satisfaction** view of the atonement was created by Anselm of Canterbury, and was very influential on the modern views of atonement. Anselm suggested that we humans owed God a debt of honor due to our rebellion and sinfulness. This could only be made right if a man acting on behalf of men repaid the debt. However, this could not be accomplished by a normal man because of our spiritual gravity and sinful natures; thus God took human form in Jesus, and paid the debt of honor back to God the Father on our behalf. So the primary difference between the satisfaction view and the ransom view is that in the case of the satisfaction view, it is God to whom the debt is repaid rather than Satan.

The third view is called **penal substitution**, and is the dominant modern view in the Western Church. This view was developed by the Reformers and the Catholic theologian Thomas Aquinas. A special case of the satisfaction view, this argues that in order for God to forgive the sins of mankind, punishment had to be taken so that God could remain just. Thus in order to satisfy God's justice, Jesus by His own choice took the punishment on Himself that we deserved, dying for our sins.

It is possible that one of these theologies describes how substitutionary atonement works; it is also possible none of them do so. What is clear from the Scriptures and Christian history is the teaching that Jesus died as a substitution for us, and that this act of His places grace inside of us, the "spiritual force" we discussed in chapter three. It is not a work we could have done for ourselves, but rather something He had to do for us. As we saw in chapter three, the only "energy" or work we can provide simply accelerates our spiritual collapse; it is only by His intervention that we are again brought into balance and avoid self-immolation.

Christ, the Great Composite, overlaminates our defective nature. He carries the load of the specifications (Law) so that we do not have to do so. And by His action we are made right before God the Father, and returned to our proper relationship with our Creator.

NINE

CALVIN & HOBBES AND HEAT TRANSFER

My favorite comic strip growing up as a kid was *Calvin & Hobbes*. I still own several books of these strips, and they never cease to amuse me. The rich world of make-believe Calvin created for himself (Spaceman Spiff and Stupendous Man in particular) perfectly captured my day-dreaming and curiosity as a child. One of my favorite ongoing plotlines was the ineptitude with which Calvin's father explains scientific principles. I can recall him saying that the Theory of Relativity only works going west (because of time zones), that the sun is the size of a quarter and physically sets in Arizona each day, and that bridges are load-rated by driving bigger and bigger trucks until the bridge falls apart. In one of my favorites, Calvin asks his dad why ice floats. The dad says that ice is cold and wants to get warm, so it goes to the top of liquids to be closer to the sun. It is after this answer that Calvin realizes he should just look these things up for himself to begin with, if he wants to get at the truth of the matter.

The questions Calvin asked were exactly the kind of things which fascinated me as a child. I can recall asking my parents why, if we doubled the amount of food in the microwave it required a longer cooking time but not when we did so in the oven. I remember asking how air conditioners and refrigerators could possibly cool down air. I remember wondering why an outside temperature of 99 degrees feels so miserable, if our bodies are 98.6 degrees inside anyway.

I would guess that for many sci-fi geeks, like me, the love of physics began when we first started to realize the power of converting one form of energy to another. When it truly "clicked" in my head that all of our great devices really do nothing but change one form of energy into another, it truly fascinated me. For me, this happened when I was doing a geography report on nuclear energy; my grandfather connected me with some engineering contacts at a nearby nuclear reactor. What I learned from them was fascinating.

I knew, of course, that the computer I was using to type my report was operating because its circuitboards were being powered by electrical power. What I did not know was that the electrical power which was traveling down a cord from the wall originated from a nuclear power plant miles away. In the power plant, this electricity was generated when a series of magnets were rotated around a coil of wire. The magnets were able to rotate because the shaft they were connected to was spinning. The shaft was spinning because it was connected to a series of turbines which were spinning. Those turbines were spinning because steam was passing by them. The steam was passing by them because water had been heated up until it changed into a gas. The water was heated up when an atom of uranium was forced to undergo radioactive decay, releasing heat energy as it decayed to a lower state. Each of these energy-change steps were necessary in order for me to turn on my computer.

But having the computer turned on was not enough; I had to do the typing. I can type because of the burning of biochemical fats stored in my body (the amount of energy used to burn these fats is measured in calories). The energy was stored in my body when I ate food. The food was either fruits and vegetables (rarely) or meats and chocolate (more commonly). In the case of fruits and vegetables, these grow to be used for food because of the heat radiated to them by the sun—which underwent a nuclear reaction in its core to generate the heat. In the case of meat, it was taken from animals who ultimately receive their energy from the same plants and, therefore, the sun as well.

Once I mapped it out (of course I did; I'm a geek), I began to see the big picture of just how complex the conversion processes were to change the energy of the sun and the nuclear energy within the atom into something as simple as typing on a computer. I loved the cleverness with which humans transferred energy from one source to the other.

One of the fundamental laws of nature is that we cannot actually create or destroy energy, but merely can change it from one form to the other. When the energy in question is thermal (heat) energy, we call this "heat transfer."

Heat transfer is a fascinating subject, because it is absolutely everywhere in your life. It is heat transfer which changes the gasoline in your car into forward motion; it is heat transfer which provides the electricity for everything that you do; it is heat transfer which cools your house; it is heat transfer which melts the ice in your drink; it is heat transfer which converts your food into exercise.

Essentially, heat transfers from one source to another by one of four basic processes: *conduction, convection, radiation*, and *phase-change*.

Conduction is the process where heat transfers between two objects which are in direct contact. The microscopic atoms in the hot object are vibrating with energy, and this vibration transfers to the neighboring objects, thus spreading the heat of the source throughout the object by physical molecular contact. One of the results of the Second Law of Thermodynamics is that heat can never spontaneously flow from a cold object to a hotter object. The transfer of heat is always in the direction moving away from the heat "source" toward the heat "sink." An example of conduction heat transfer is when you put a skillet on your stove-top: the stove is heated electrically and then the physical contact between the skillet and the stove-top transfers the heat of the stove-top to the skillet. Another good example is the loss of heat out of an unsealed window in your home; the cold air outside is touching the hot air inside, so the heat transfers out of your house and "heats the whole neighborhood," as your dad liked to say.

Convection is the transfer of heat from one place to another based upon the movement of fluids (either gases or liquids). For example, consider your fireplace. When you begin burning the logs (converting their stored potential energy into heat energy), the heat departs the burning logs and transfers to the fluid (air) surrounding it. Increased temperature produces lower density, so the hotter fluid begins to rise and spread. As it mixes with the cooler air around it, conduction begins and the heat is transferred from the hotter air to the cooler surrounding air, until everything is of the same temperature.

The third type of heat transfer comes as **thermal radiation**. Thermal radiation is when electromagnetic waves travel from a hot object to a cooler object, thus transferring energy. The heating of the Earth by the Sun is one example. Your microwave heating up a Hot Pocket is another example: the microwaves released carry a very high amount of heat, which is absorbed by the food.

Phase-change is the fourth type of heat transfer. Whenever an object changes from one phase to another (e.g., solid to liquid or liquid to gas), heat energy is used and this can be exploited by engineers.

Understanding heat transfer answered many of those nagging questions I had as a youth.

Putting extra food in the microwave requires more time to heat because the microwave sends radioactive waves into the food. The more substance you are heating, the more time (and thus, quantity of microwave radiation) you need.

Air conditioners work by taking advantage of the phase-change method of heat transfer. Hot air flows over a series of evaporator coils, which contain a very cold refrigerant chemical. The air loses heat into the cold coils, thus "cooling" the air down. This heat results in the liquid refrigerant converting into a gaseous state. The gas is transferred into compressor coils, where it is compressed back down to high-pressure, resulting in a conversion back to liquid form (the excess heat generated is evacuated to the outside air). This liquid then moves back to the evaporator coils, where it is ready for the introduction of more hot air.

We are uncomfortable in weather which is close to our body temperature because our body needs to remove heat and transfer it to the surrounding air. When the temperature difference between our body and the surrounding air is large (as it is on cool days), the heat transfers very efficiently and we feel comfortable. But on a hot day, the heat differential between your internal body temperature and the surrounding air is not large enough for efficient heat transfer. Your body begins getting too hot inside and must resort to more desperate measures (you start sweating profusely) in an attempt to more quickly remove heat from your body. The risk of heat stroke and death is particularly high when the outside temperature exceeds your body's internal temperature. Recall that heat cannot transfer from cold to hot, so the direction of heat flow in this situation is inward. The outside temperature will raise your internal body temperature, potentially resulting in serious consequences to your health.

Learning heat transfer is fascinating, because when you look around you it is everywhere.

+ + + theology: justification + + +

In the last chapter, we saw that Jesus' death on the cross served as a substitutionary atonement for us; just as the reinforcement of a failed structure frees substandard components from needing to meet their specifications, so too did His death serve to take the weight of the Law off of mankind and free us from our own sinfulness.

In chapter three, I argued by analogy that humans had a natural tendency to turn inward inevitability toward of self-destruction. I called this sinful nature "spiritual gravity." I then said that there was inside us a spiritual force—the grace of God—pushing outward in an attempt to counteract and eventually overcome our natural spiritual gravitation. I described this spiritual force as being similar to a hot gas, expanding outward and fighting against the gravitational collapse.

All Christians agree that the spiritual force of grace comes to us from God: not unlike heat transfer, it originates solely with the Source (God) and transfers only in one direction, to the sink (us). Just as the laws of thermodynamics prevent a cool object from radiating heat to a hotter object, so too do the laws of the spiritual world prevent us from radiating grace to God. All of the grace forming our "spiritual force" and overcoming our natural spiritual gravitation gets inside of us by being transferred from the Source of this grace or heat. (Interestingly, the Bible also compares the Holy Spirit to a fire or heat inside of our souls—Acts 2:1-4, 1 Thess 5:19.)

All branches of Christianity are in agreement that God is the sole source of this grace transfer, a process which they call *justification* – God's act of declaring a sinner righteous based not upon the sinner's works, but the work of Christ on the cross. The question arises when we debate exactly how this transfer of grace occurs. There are two primary theological explanations for how this transfer occurs: *imputed righteousness* and *infused righteousness.*

Recall that we discussed the four different methods of heat transfer? Let us use two of those as analogies to understand this transfer of grace out of God's infinite supply and into our spirits.

Imputed righteousness, as taught by the Lutherans, Calvinists, and other Protestant bodies, says that the righteousness of God is completely alien to mankind. Mankind never did any good work to earn the righteousness: man's actions contribute to spiritual gravitational collapse, and it is only by the presence of God's grace that this is overcome and we change into the person whom we are meant to be. That is, righteousness is *imputed* or transferred to us. Consider this to be sort of like grace "conduction." Just as heat conduction happens only between two objects which are in physical contact, the grace comes from Christ alone, and it is only when we are in contact with Him that grace flows from Him to us.

The concept of imputation of righteousness says that when we are saved, God "places our skillet on His stove," as it were: grace flows completely from Him to us, and will continue doing so until He runs out. (And since the Source is infinite, it will never run out!) From a practical standpoint, this means that you did nothing to earn justification before God, and you can do nothing to lose it. Sins committed after justification may result in your punishment, but they cannot separate you from Him or His grace—no more than throwing a piece of ice onto a hot skillet can turn the stove off. Because you are in direct contact with Him through His Spirit dwelling within you, His grace will always flow into your heart and transfer like heat into your soul. This grace inside of you serves as the spiritual force which overcomes and then eventually (after mortal death) eliminates the spiritual gravitation of your sinful nature.

The opposing view, held most popularly by the Catholics, is that of **infused grace**. This we can compare to our phase-change heat transfer from earlier in the chapter. Recall that a refrigerant in your air conditioner is changed from liquid to gas by the passing of hot air along the coils. This is the same concept as taught by Augustine and Catholicism: when Christ's death atones for your sacrifice and you believe in Him, your very being is changed into a different phase. In this new phase, you are capable of transferring your own heat (good works) without Him providing any additional heat to you.

Recall that the refrigerant, once changed into a gas, must still travel within the compressor coils. These coils seek to compress the gas back into a liquid. In the same way, the Catholics say that the world around us constantly fights against our new nature in Christ, wishing to compress us back into our old forms. If we are not diligent, we can commit sins which are bad enough (mortal sins) to undo our newfound relationship with Christ and return us to our original phase, lacking in His grace. The Catholics see the sacraments (baptism, confession, the Eucharist, etc.) and good works as methods of continuing to receive His grace and avoid compressing back into our prior state.

So even though Catholics and Protestants both agree that the grace begins with God and is transferred to us completely by the work of Christ's sacrifice, there remains a great practical difference with regard to how the grace is transferred. If transferred via a sort of grace conduction, as the Protestants believe, then once you have been justified, you cannot lose this relationship. No sin you perform is bad enough that it can separate you from God, for the heat of grace is continuously transferring into your soul through your connection to Christ. Yet if you believe in a sort of grace phase-change, as do the Catholics (and, to an extent, Methodists), then you must be wary of your actions and works. Failure to perform good works, or sins of significant evil, could result in losing that which was once obtained in Christ.

This difference became a key theological wedge in the Protestant Reformation. Five Latin phrases, called the **Five Solas**, began to spread during the Reformation to summarize the key differences between the Reformers and the Catholics. The five solas are: *sola scriptura, sola fide, sola gratia, solo Christo, soli Deo gloria*; these mean, respectively, "by Scripture alone," "by faith alone," "by grace alone," "through Christ alone," and "glory to God alone." These were seen as separating Catholicism from Protestantism, and are useful to our discussion of grace.

Sola fide: Protestants, believing in a sort of grace conduction, believed that justification came solely based upon the believer's faith in

Christ, and was not dependent upon the performing of any rite, ritual, or good work. By contrast, Catholicism taught that grace was granted by infusion via the sacraments, and failure to partake in sacraments as well as certain sins could undo the "phase change."

Sola gratia: Protestants taught that salvation came by unmerited favor (grace) only, with which the Catholics agree. But Protestants took it further, saying that any future good works were only due to the grace being conducted to the Christian by God; this differs from the Catholic teaching, which says that justification fundamentally changes the person so that now they are capable of meriting greater grace for themselves based upon their actions.

Solo Christo: Protestants, believing in a conduction of grace, taught that no other source of grace existed. That is, the only source of the grace transfer was the contact with Jesus Christ as the one Mediator. They call this the "universal priesthood" of the believer: all baptized Christians are connected to Christ directly, and this is the source of grace. This was at odds with Catholic teaching, which is the belief that sacraments had to be administered by ordained priests of the Catholic faith in order to properly transmit grace to the believer, and further that Mary and the saints were capable of mediating to God on behalf of the believer.

Soli Deo gloria: The Protestants taught that because every good we do is conducted to us by the grace of God via our connection to Christ, we are due none of the glory for our good works. Good things that we do are nothing but God working through us. By comparison, since Catholics believed some of their good works were of their own volition post-conversion, then some of the glory would go to the individual rather than God.

Sola scriptura: The Protestants taught that the Bible alone was the source of Christian doctrine, and requires no interpretation outside of itself to understand its core doctrines. This is in opposition to the Catholics and Orthodox churches, which state that only those ordained through Apostolic Succession may properly teach on the Scripture. This group, called the *Magisterium*, is the combined knowledge of the bishops. Though *sola scriptura* does not directly relate to the discussion of grace and justification, it is the basic principle which led to the other four *solas*: if you accept *sola scriptura*, then the other four *solas* are likely to be the interpretation of the Bible which you will eventually reach. It is the extra-Biblical teachings of the Magisterium which lead to the Catholic belief system.

While Catholics and Protestants do disagree significantly on how grace is transferred to us (and this difference is important as it has practical influence on some of your actions), all agree that the grace originates from God. God is the Source of our grace, just as every heat transfer problem begins with a heat source; and we believers are the heat "sink" which receives the grace, just as in any heat transfer problem the heat must eventually end up transferring somewhere.

This transfer of "heat" into our hearts, via the receipt of the Holy Spirit, results in us gaining an internal spiritual force to battle against our spiritual gravity (sinful nature). It first overcomes our gravitation (a process called justification). But in any heat transfer problem, we know that eventually a state of thermal equilibrium will be reached, when no more heat can transfer from the source to the sink. The same is true in Christian theology. As God's grace continues to be transferred to us through our lives, we undergo a process called *sanctification*, in which we are made holy before Him. Eventually we will be transformed from the cold sinners we are into creatures of magnificent grace, co-heirs to Christ and immortal beings living with Him for eternity. This is the *Gospel*, or good news, of our Lord Jesus Christ.

– TEN –

SCHRODINGER'S CHRISTIAN

If you are a science-fiction geek like me then you probably have heard at least in passing of the Schrodinger's Cat thought experiment. Unfortunately, virtually every time it is described in films or television, Hollywood gets it wrong. We will clarify this, but first we need to do a little bit of study on quantum mechanics.

Until you get to about the third year of university-level physics, everything you have studied is called classical physics. Classical physics uses the laws of Newton and Kepler and Galileo to define the world around us. These laws work really well except in the very extremes of natural situations (extremes which we have only begun exploring in the last century or so). At one extreme are very massive or very fast-moving objects, the realm of Einstein's theories of relativity, a fascinating weirdness which we will discuss in chapter fifteen. At the other end of the spectrum, the smallest end, is the field of quantum mechanics. Quantum mechanics is the study of really, really small things -- the study of events and matter on atomic and subatomic scales.

Classical physicists have historically seen the world in a very specific way. First, we assumed that as we got more and more powerful microscopes, we would eventually find the tiny particle of which everything else is made. Second, we viewed energy as waves (microwaves, gamma waves, etc.) and matter as particles (protons, neutrons, electrons, or some other physical object of a measurable size). Third, we assumed that the universe was ruled by deterministic formulae: if you could understand the mathematics and do the research, you would be able to predict the behavior of any particle with complete accuracy. As Einstein once said, "God does not play with dice" – the universe is ruled by natural laws, whether we understand them or not.

Quantum mechanics, however, has thrown these assumptions into chaos in the past century.

As we gained more and more sophisticated techniques for observing the tiniest corners of reality, we found a few surprising things. One is that matter seems to have both wave and particle characteristics—it is neither wave nor particle, but both. Another is that certain actions at the subatomic level seem to be completely probabilistic in nature, rather than deterministic: in other words, there seems to be no underlying law controlling the actions of the particles, but rather they seem to react based upon probability density curves. As an example, perhaps you design an experiment in which you are shooting a subatomic particle through a certain slit: 70% of the time it would go left, and 30% it would go right. It is possible to predict the probabilities of the population, but impossible to accurately predict the behavior of each individual particle. Mathematically, all we can do for an individual particle is describe it probabilistically ("it is 70% likely to go left"). If we ran the experiment a million times, this particle would go left about 700,000 times and right about 300,000 times.

Of course, this is very uncomfortable for those of us with a classical physics mindset. We prefer to believe that if we knew the equations and all the inputs, we could predict everything that will ever happen in any situation. Yet on the subatomic scale, it appears that this is not the case, and the probability nature of particles is not the result of a lack of knowledge but rather a fundamental reality of how the world works.

The situation is even more puzzling when we begin to consider the influence of time. You see, in physics, the laws work the same whether running forward or backward. The motion of a ball thrown into the air is the same whether we study the ball in reverse or in normal time. From a physics standpoint, time is irrelevant to the calculations: it is only due to entropy that we have a concept of a "direction" of time pointing from past to future (more on this subject in chapter eleven).

Yet this is not the case with subatomic particles. What happened in a particle's past can no longer be changed (it is not probabilistic, but determined already); yet the future seems to be based on probabilities rather than mathematical certainty. You cannot run the physics backward equally as well as running it forward, for the "backward" direction is settled and the "forward" direction is uncertain. This is a completely unique phenomenon. In no other case in all of physics do we see this happen.

So physicists at first were understandably a bit puzzled. Here they seem to see that the mathematics only works repeatedly in the "past" direction; in the future we must rely on probabilities when dealing with subatomic particles.

Bring back out your Flatland paper from chapter one, flip it over, and let us do another little thought experiment to help illustrate the situation.

Along the bottom, draw a time axis: the left of the paper is time $t=0$, and the right of the paper is time $t=100$. This will be the life-line of our pretend particle. Let us assume that right now, we are halfway through its life (time $t=50$). Between $t=0$ and $t=50$, draw the motion history of the particle. It can be whatever you want: a straight line, a sine wave, whatever. This is a single, solid, unbroken line: it is the "past" of the particle. But looking to the future, the particle exists as an uncertain probability. So let us draw this section, from $t=50$ to $t=100$. Recall that 70% of the time the particle is going to turn "left" (up, on your page) and 30% of the time it will turn "right" (down, on your page). So I want you to draw two paths: one going down and one going up. Now, I want you to draw six more "up" paths very close to the first "up" path, and two more "down" paths very close to the first "down" path.

What you now have is a history of your make-believe particle. In the past, we have only a straight line: the path which it took from its birth ($t=0$) until now ($t=50$). But going in the future on your page ($t=50$ thru $t=100$), it exists only as probability: there are ten possible paths, 70% of which go "left" and 30% of which go "right." You see that its future, rather than being solid and certain is "fuzzy": a combination of possible realities.

Now, let us move to phase two of the experiment.

Pretend that you observe the particle as it moves from $t=50$ to $t=75$. (We will pretend that it went "right.") So now erase all paths from $t=50$ to $t=75$ except for the one that you are pretending the path took. So now you should have a solid line all the way from $t=0$ to $t=75$. From $t=75$ to $t=100$, then, you should see the three "right" paths connected to where you are now, and seven "left" paths unconnected to anything. Since your particle cannot jump back left again, you can erase the "left" paths completely.

So now your particle's life is certain from $t=0$ to $t=75$, not just $t=50$ as before; it remains fuzzy from $t=75$ to $t=100$. What changed? We "observed" the behavior from $t=50$ to $t=75$, so the ten "fuzzy" paths it could have taken during this time are no longer valid; now it can only have taken the path which we observed. If we "run the math backwards," there are no longer ten paths between $t=50$ and $t=75$; there is just the one path.

This is called the "collapse" of the waveform. The path of this particle once existed as ten probable paths: but after being observed, the system can no longer return to a probability-based system. Now it can only work as it was already observed to work.

This is what was so confusing to physicists. It appears that the future exists as potential waveforms rather than a set future; yet, as we move from past to present to future, the potentials go away and only what we observed to be true is actually true. How can we explain this? Why would reality work this way, where our actual act of observation is changing the mathematics? There are several common interpretation models to explain this phenomenon.

The *Copenhagen interpretation* is the most commonly-held interpretation by modern physicists. It was developed by Niels Bohr and Werner Heisenberg while working in Copenhagen in the 1920s. In this interpretation, the situation we described is the way reality works. The future for a subatomic particle really does exist as more than one possible form at the same time: it is only the act of observation which "collapses" the waveform into its now-true nature.

This actually meshes naturally with how most humans see the world: the future is unset (some things are more likely than others, but nothing is perfectly determined yet), but after we live through (observe) the events, then they are now set in stone as a "true" past. The past cannot be changed, but the future can be any number of different things. Someone could have killed Hitler in 1940 and it would have changed the course of history; instead of taking the path it did, it would have chosen a different path from among its future "waveforms." But after 1940 passed and Hitler was still alive, then no one could ever change the fact that he lived through 1940. So the future is uncertain until it is observed; then it becomes "past" and can no longer change.

So to those who hold the Copenhagen interpretation, the future of a subatomic particle is not determined until it is observed. It is our observation which changes something from "future potential" to "past and certain." However, this has consequences. Remember that I said that mathematics and physics can run in both directions equally well. In other words, in a very real sense, all of those future situations must actually really exist as realities: the other realities are "destroyed" once we observe and collapse the waveform.

While Copenhagen is by far the most common interpretation, there are other interpretive methods as well. One which is commonly used in science fiction is the "many-worlds" interpretation, which states that each of the different paths form different parallel universes. Each act of observation splits the universe into a number of parallel universes, 70% of which saw our particle go left and 30% of which saw it go right. So there were times where Hitler won the war and times that he did not, and we are (thankfully) the descendents of those who observed one timeline in which he did not.

Being merely a humble geek and not a theoretical physicist, I cannot say whether the Copenhagen interpretation (or any other) is actually correct, and we will explore some of these quantum concepts in more detail in a later chapter. For now, all that is important is the understanding that the most common interpretation is the Copenhagen interpretation.

One person who was not a fan of the Copenhagen interpretation was Albert Einstein, and another was a good friend of his, Austrian physicist Erwin Schrodinger. In 1935, Schrodinger was responding to one of Einstein's papers questioning the Copenhagen interpretation. In the response, Schrodinger created a thought experiment called Schrodinger's Cat which has become a staple of understanding quantum physics because of the clever way in which it represents the interpretation:

> *"One can even set up quite ridiculous cases. A cat is penned up in a steel chamber, along with the following device (which must be secured against direct interference by the cat): in a*

Geiger counter, there is a tiny bit of radioactive substances, so small that perhaps in the course of the hour, one of the atoms decays, but also, with equal probability, perhaps none; if it happens, the counter tube discharges, and through a relay releases a hammer that shatters a small flask of hydrocyanic acid. If one has left this entire system to itself for an hour, one would say that the cat still lives if meanwhile no atom has decayed. The psi-function of the entire system would express this by having in it the living and dead cat (pardon the expression) mixed or smeared out in equal parts." (Erwin Schrodinger).

So Schrodinger makes a thought experiment to show what he believes is the ridiculousness of the Copenhagen interpretation. He says let us pretend that instead of a particle, you have a cat in a box who has exactly a 50/50 chance of living; to use quantum physics terms, the cat could be represented as a waveform with a 50% chance of being alive and dead. According to the Copenhagen interpretation, the cat actually, really exists in both states simultaneously until someone observes it: it is literally both simultaneously living and dead. Only the act of observation actually forces reality to choose one outcome or the other.

Now of course, quantum mechanics does not say that this would happen in the case that Schrodinger sets up! They speak only of subatomic particles, not felines. But Schrodinger's point was to assail the flaw that he saw in believing that there is no true reality other than probability. Schrodinger called it arrogant to accept a "blurred model for representing reality...there is a difference between a shaky or out-of-focus photograph and a snapshot of clouds and fog banks."

In Schrodinger's view (and Einstein's), the Copenhagen interpretation was absurd. The observer did not change reality; the situation was simply that we did not properly understand the laws and observations yet. We were using a blurred model, and treating it as if it was a crisp photograph. In rebuttal, Copenhagen physicists believe that they have explanations for Schrodinger's Cat, as do many-worlds physicists. Indeed, the more we learn, the more physicists become converted to the Copenhagen interpretation.

Regardless of the physics debate, Schrodinger's Cat thought experiment has become a sort of litmus test for any quantum analysis. It was brilliant in its absurdity and its elegance, and has also gained widespread use in popular culture. It is discussed in books by authors like Douglas Adams and Robert Heinlein, as well as on television series and movies as diverse as *Doctor Who*, *The Big Bang Theory*, and *Flashforward*. There is just something fascinating about imagining the poor cat sitting there, both living and dead at the same time.

+ + + theology: simul justus et peccator + + +

As to which quantum interpretation (if any) is correct, I cannot say. But what I do find interesting is this concept of waveform duality and the influence of the observer in creating and forming the reality of a situation. I find this fascinating because it is almost exactly what Martin Luther described when he talked about the life of a converted Christian.

In Catholic theology, recall that they taught an infused righteousness: after conversion the believer was changed into something fundamentally different than he had been originally. His baptism washed away his sinfulness. Catholics would teach that the Christian still has an inclination for sin ("concupiscence"), but that it does not become sin until it is performed. When it does become sin, this must be forgiven through the sacramental administration of grace. To use my analogy of heat transfer, the Catholics taught that at the moment grace was transferred to a person, he underwent a phase change and was now a fundamentally new creature, his spiritual gravity perfectly offset by the already-received grace. As long as the person avoids the "compression coils" (temptations) of the world which would turn them back into their prior liquid form ("sinner"), they would remain saved. While saved, then, they were not truly sinners; or at least, the potential to live perfectly was now present.

Luther and the Reformers saw a different concept in Scripture and human nature. They did not look at the life of a Christian and find someone who was changed from "basically sinful" to "basically good." Luther and others saw in human nature an ongoing spiritual gravitation, an ongoing selfishness, which was not removed at the time of conversion in any believer. Luther argued that our sinful nature remained unchanged after our conversion. Citing a number of statements from Scripture, he argued that we are *simul justus et peccator*: simultaneously righteous and sinner. In some fundamental way, Luther says, we are justified *despite remaining as a sinner*.

In Luther's *simul justus et peccator* argument, I see shades of Schrodinger's Cat. Quantum mechanics sees the universe as made not of deterministic particles but rather a sort of blurry waveform, which observation forces to take a single reality. In the same way, Luther says that each of our souls is a sort of waveform: simultaneously righteous and sinner. Becoming a Christian did not remove the potential for sin or the reality that we will continue to be sinners; rather, becoming a Christian is a promise. It is God's promise that when we are viewed by the Great Observer in the last judgment, and our waveform is forced to collapse into one reality or the other, we can be confident it will collapse to reveal not our own sinful nature, but rather the perfect righteousness of Jesus Christ.

Just as Schrodinger's Cat is simultaneously living and dead, so too are all Christians simultaneously living in the spirit and dead in the flesh. But these two forms, though they co-exist now, will one day be judged. And if a non-Christian is judged, God will look at him and see only one possible state of collapse: not being bonded to Christ, the non-Christian being viewed has no choice but to be seen only as the selfish sinful flesh. For the Christians, however, when God sees us He sees a waveform, not simply one pathway. To God, we exist both as our own sinful choices and as the righteousness of Christ. Thus we have a natural duality, a wave-form: just like with the particle lifeline you drew earlier, we are a blurry line which combines our sinful nature with Jesus' sinless nature. And just like any quantum waveform, once we are observed our duality will collapse into one single reality.

The Gospel of Christ is a promise to us: a promise that, if we believe in Jesus and follow Him, then when we are Observed during the final judgment our duality will collapse in a predictable way. It is a promise that God will see the righteous life of Jesus Christ and the Holy Spirit who has acted through us, rather than our sinful nature. Just as the observation of a quantum particle makes its potential futures collapse into a permanent reality, so too would the observation by the Judge on the last day cause our duality to collapse into its infinitely permanent state.

Luther's *simul justus et peccator* philosophy remains opposed by Catholicism, but is believed in some form or the other by all Protestants. It is largely based upon Paul's passage in Romans 7, in which he discusses his ongoing duality after becoming justified in Christ. As Paul says,

> *"For we know that the law is spiritual, but I am of the flesh, sold under sin. For I do not understand my own actions. For I do not do what I want, but I do the very thing I hate. Now if I do what I do not want, I agree with the law, that it is good. So now it is no longer I who do it, but sin that dwells within me. For I know that nothing good dwells in me, that is, in my flesh. For I have the desire to do what is right, but not the ability to carry it out. For I do not do the good I want, but the evil I do not want is what I keep on doing....Wretched man that I am! Who will deliver me from this body of death?" (Romans 7:14-20,24)*

Herein we see Luther's theology stated quite well. Paul has been a justified believer for many years at this time, yet he still teaches that a duality exists between his flesh and spirit. The spirit wishes him to follow God's law and live righteously, but even despite the grace given him by God, he is incapable of carrying this out, because "nothing good" dwells in his flesh. He needs deliverance from the body of death, which only Jesus Christ can offer (v.25).

Or, to say it another way: the waveform of his soul is dual in nature, being at the same time both the sinful nature of his flesh and the grace transferred to Him by Jesus Christ's atoning sacrifice. This duality will remain in him all of his life, and only God, as the True Observer, can cause this waveform to collapse. Then and only then will his true reality come into being: the reality of the Paul who is co-heir with Jesus.

– ELEVEN –

SPIRITUAL ENTROPY

We will delve deeper to the weirdness of quantum mechanics in chapter twelve, but for a brief respite let us return to the safe world of thermodynamics for a bit. (We engineers can only handle so much theoretical physics without a break.)

Thermodynamics, the study of energy, is immensely useful and practical (as we discussed in chapter nine). One of the cornerstones of thermodynamics is the Second Law of Thermodynamics, which stands as one of the most thoroughly-proved laws in all of science. The first law of thermodynamics serves to define thermodynamic energy, but it is in the second law that we get to the meat of the science. At a very broad level, the second law of thermodynamics states that over time, differences in energy levels of an isolated system will tend to equalize. In practical terms, the second law makes three very specific claims: you can't buy a perfect refrigerator; you can't buy a perfect engine; and today is always worse than yesterday.

What do I mean by each? Let us see.

You can't buy a perfect refrigerator. The first key result of the second law of thermodynamics is that heat will never spontaneously flow from a cold object to a hot object. In order for an object's temperature to lower, it must give off heat to a colder object; it can never give off heat to a warmer object. So for example, if you place your ice in room-temperature lemonade, the lemonade will give off heat to the ice, until the lemonade is cooled down and the ice is melted; the heat will continue to transfer from hot to cold until temperature equilibrium is reached. The hotter the external temperature, the hotter the lemonade; therefore, the gap in temperature between the ice and the lemonade is greater, and thus the ice will melt faster as the lemonade cools from very hot to just lukewarm. The implication is that you can never create a perfect refrigerator: there is never a situation where an object can get colder without either having energy put into the system (taking advantage of the phase-change properties that we discussed in chapter nine), or by being surrounded by a colder object. There is no refrigerator you can invent which sits there, with no outside power source, and continues to cool off the things inside it. Eventually the refrigerator will continue to take on the heat of the surrounding air until it is at a temperature equilibrium.

You can't buy a perfect engine. The second result of the second law of thermodynamics is that it is impossible to extract all of the heat from a heat source and use it to do practical work. Any time you transfer heat from a hot source and use it to do work, some amount of heat will be lost to the colder reservoir surrounding the hot. As a result, you can never get perfectly energy-efficient engines. This is not some small, insignificant amount of inefficiency, either. In a typical modern internal combustion engine, the peak energy efficiency is something like 30%. About 70% of the heat generated from the fuel combustion is lost as heat that did not actually turn the crankshaft (35% of the original heat is carried away in the exhaust pipe, and 35% is radiated away to the outside air).

Today is always worse than yesterday. The third result is one which is often misunderstood and yet very important; this is the concept known as entropy, and we will discuss entropy at some length here.

Entropy is the measurement of how much of the total energy of a system is *not* available for conversion into useful work. For example, let us say that we took our room-temperature lemonade and isolated it from the outside hot air so that no extra energy can go in or out. We then drop our cold ice cube into the drink. At this point, the entropy of the system is very low: that is, there is still a very high percentage of the internal heat (within the lemonade) available to do work. As time passes, however, more and more of the heat energy has transferred to the ice, melting it; we have grown closer and closer to a state of equilibrium. As a result, we would say that the entropy (proportion of unavailable energy) has now increased in our system. There is less available thermal energy to apply to doing the work of melting the ice cube.

Applied to the internal combustion engine, we see that at the moment of combustion we have the lowest entropy. All of the thermal energy is available to do work. But over time, the heat begins to dissipate into the engine cooling system and less and less energy is available to do work. The entropy has increased.

Put another way, you could say that entropy is a measure of a system's disorder. Consider a sand castle, for example. The sand is piled high into a perfect sand castle, and thus the sand has stored within it a potential energy due to its height off of the ground. It has low entropy: a high percentage of the sand's potential energy is available to do work. But given time, the sand castle will collapse, and the sand will be scattered on the lower ground, leaving no potential energy to be convertible into work. As a result, the entropy, or disorder, or lack of available energy, has increased.

The second law of thermodynamics says that in an isolated system (one which does not receive any outside energy), entropy will always tend to either stay the same or increase. That is, without external energy being provided, systems will never self-organize or spontaneously develop a higher percentage of energy for doing more work.

So for example, you will never see sand build itself into a sand castle; only if external energy is applied can this occur. You will never see a car engine gain heat from the cooler surrounding air and therefore have a higher availability for work. You will never drop a cube of ice into a hot glass of lemonade and see the ice begin to expand while the remaining lemonade gets hotter. You will never see shards of ceramic rise from the ground and form into a coffee mug.

This is why I say of entropy, "today is always worse than yesterday" – given time, any isolated system will dissipate energy and move toward a state of lower energy and more disorder. Eventually any system ends in what is called "heat death"—the highest state of entropy, where all heat energy is spread equally and at the lowest possible availability, so that literally nothing can occur.

What most people do not realize is that this appears to be where we get our concept of time. We can look at a picture of a beach with scattered sand, then a picture of a beach with a sand castle, and put these in the proper order of time. That is, entropy is the physical process which provides the "time's arrow" for our minds. As time goes on and heat transfers take place within our body (resulting in our hearts beating and our minds working), and we see the effects of the time's arrow around us, we notice the passing of time.

We can all make changes to a system to reverse the effects of entropy...but only temporarily, and only at an overall cost to the system. If I took my laptop and sat inside a perfectly isolated box, receiving no energy from outside the system, I could create local organization: I could type to create these words on the screen. But in so doing, I have actually created increased entropy, and a total loss for the system. For although the computer file I am typing into became more orderly, I used my own energy (which came from food) to do so, leaving less available food energy for work; furthermore I used battery power from my computer, again leaving less energy to do work. So the total entropy of the system increased: less energy is available for work, and the system as a whole is less orderly than it was before I began. Stephen Hawking, in his book *A Brief History of Time*, estimated that to read his book would give you two million bits of information, but in doing so you generated a disorder increase of twenty million million million million bits. Anything we do results in the use of energy and ultimately makes the system less orderly than before, leaving less energy available to do work.

+ + + theology: sanctification + + +

As we discussed in the last chapter, after being justified Christians continue to live on in a sort of waveform, capable of doing both evil and good; this waveform will not collapse into a truly righteous soul until God observes us at the final judgment. While we are living here we continue to be, as Luther put it, *simul justus et peccator*, simultaneously sinner and righteous.

Sanctification is the process by which a justified Christian is made holy. Peter describes this process by saying:

> "[S]upplement your faith with virtue, and virtue with knowledge, and knowledge with self-control, and self-control with steadfastness, and steadfastness with godliness, and

godliness with brotherly affection, and brotherly affection with love." (2 Pet 1:5-7)

Paul describes the results of the process of sanctification (which he calls the "fruits of the spirit") as "love, joy, peace, patience, kindness, goodness, faithfulness, gentleness, self-control" (Gal 5:22-23).

So the question for every Christian, after having believed in Jesus Christ and accepting His atoning sacrifice for our justification, is simply: how do I become more holy?

In chapter three, we described our sinful nature as a sort of spiritual gravitation, constantly collapsing in on ourselves; in chapters eight through ten, we demonstrated that this does not cease after becoming a Christian but continues. So how does one reverse this collapsing effect, and begin instead to grow more holy, more Christlike; how do we turn the process around and have the spiritual gravitation actually reverse and move away from us?

According to the Methodists and the Catholics, who believe that their righteousness was infused into them as a phase-change grace transfer, this is accomplished through acts of willpower, diligence, spiritual discipline, and the proper administration of sacramental rites. I will not spend much time on this theology; as you can tell from my previous chapters, I find this to be inconsistent with the reality of human nature. But out of respect for my brothers and sisters who wish more information on this topic, you can read the *Catechism of the Catholic Church*, which gives extremely good information on their view of sanctification.

Instead, I believe the true answer is that we cannot, through willpower, make ourselves more righteous. As Paul demonstrated in Romans 7, there is no amount of willpower we can exert to stop our flesh from experiencing spiritual collapse. It is our natural state, for as long as we are trapped in these sinful bodies. Until God observes us in the final judgment, and we are given our new bodies (more on this in later chapters), we cannot overcome the reality of spiritual gravity. Our flesh will always tend toward collapse.

Pure willpower is a dangerous way to go about trying to become more holy. I love the story *Dr. Jekyll and Mr. Hyde*, by Robert Louis Stevenson. Though he was not a Christian, Stevenson's book is as good as Luther at describing the duality of man. Dr. Jekyll concocts a potion which allows him to separate into the two aspects of his nature, the altruistic Dr. Jekyll and the depraved Mr. Hyde. Eventually Jekyll chooses to cast off Hyde and lives a wholesome life for several months, doing every good work that he can. He alleviates a great many people's suffering, and is serving as a perfect, sinless man. Then one day as he is sitting on a park bench, he begins to think of all the good things he has done, and compares himself to others. At that moment – *and without drinking the potion* – he is transformed spontaneously into Mr. Hyde. This moment is the beginning of the end for Jekyll, as he eventually succumbs to Hyde's depravity.

Stevenson understood the same thing as Luther and Paul: willpower and good deeds are never able to overcome our natural selfish natures. Even when we do good, we find it impossible to avoid judging others or craving the praise of man, and thus even our good works become perverted and self-centered, turning into sin.

We humans suffer from what I call **spiritual entropy**. Over time, we are always moving toward collapse and disorder. Given enough time, our sinful natures tend increasingly toward selfishness and will always sin. No amount of self-induced energy can avoid the collapse of our lives into disorder.

We can no more build a holy life out of our sinful nature than sand can will itself into being a sand castle. Just like entropy in the physical world, spiritual entropy requires that we will always tend toward spiritual decay and selfishness.

Recall that in the physical world, we could create local examples of increasing order and energy, but only at the total cost of the system; entropy always increased in total, even if local changes had decreased entropy.

The same is true of spiritual entropy. You might, through willpower, be able to make one area of your life better. But your willpower can never do anything other than make the total system collapse toward selfishness.

Spiritual entropy demands that, left to our own devices, we will always be less holy than we were before.

Perhaps through willpower you can become very dedicated in your prayer life; but in so doing you will see some other area of your Christian holiness suffer, whether it be that you judge others or fall out of the habit of studying Scripture or neglect your family. (I cannot help remembering reading an article somewhere about Jonathan Edwards, who routinely would leave the table in the middle of supper to go pray more if he felt that he had not done enough praying that day; though his prayer life makes mine look absurd by comparison, this great increase in one area no doubt harmed his relationship with his kids and the wife who had served him by making dinner and were eager to spend time with their father.)

Perhaps through willpower you can become a great evangelist or pastor, traveling around the country and preaching to thousands, leading many to the Lord. But if it is based upon willpower, you will fail in some other area so that overall your spiritual life is on the net worse: perhaps you will become vain or obsessed with wealth (think of all the famously rich preachers with their tailored suits and $500 haircuts), or perhaps you will be a poor husband and father, or perhaps you will fall into sexual sin, or perhaps you will judge pastors whose ministries seem less effective than yours.

Perhaps you can, through willpower, sustain a diet and exercise routine; but in the process you may find that you become a bad father, or vain about your looks, or judgmental of those who fail at their diets.

I need not list the thousands of other examples, for I am quite certain you can think of some yourself. This is one of the reasons why Alcoholics Anonymous has been so successful: it is based not primarily upon willpower but upon admitting that your willpower is insufficient to control your actions, and turning over control to a higher power.

Trying to will yourself to a more spiritual or holy life will always fail. This is very visible in the Bible. If you chase after the Law with willpower, you will become hypocritical and judgmental like the Pharisees, or legalistic like the scribes, or chase a false theology like the Sadducees, or become overly concerned with politics like the Zealots, or any of a hundred other failures.

Spiritual entropy cannot be avoided. Isolated to yourself, based upon your own willpower, any local holiness which you are able to create will come at the overall expense of the system. You will always, based upon your own actions, turn judgmental and selfish and sinful.

So how are we to become holy? Well, recall that in thermodynamics, entropy applies only to an isolated system. A plant left in an isolated system will die; left in an open system, where it can receive heat energy from the Sun, it will thrive. In other words, entropy does not apply if outside energy can be added into the system.

The same is true of spiritual entropy: the receipt of outside energy is what makes spiritual entropy no longer applicable. Holiness can only come when you realize that your willpower leads to death and decay, but the grace of God in you, when you are constantly being fed by the Holy Spirit, makes you an open system. If you admit that your own sanctification is not something which *you* can achieve, and instead focus your energy on *allowing God to do the transforming*, then you will find God will work in you to make you more Christlike on a daily basis.

The answer comes, as pastor John Ortberg says, not from trying harder but from trying softer. It is allowing God to do the work in you; allowing the energy and grace which He transfers to your soul to be the guide for your holiness. Some of the changes He makes will be painful; some will take time; some will require sacrifice; some will seem to be the wrong things. But if you are allowing Him to change you from the inside-out, instead of you trying to control things from the outside-in, then you will see true change occur.

Spiritual entropy will not apply, because you are no longer an isolated system. You are not, as the Catholics would teach, simply a sinner who God changed and now you must continue to live according to the impossible laws of God or be out of His will. Rather, sanctification comes not from our will but from His; not from our effort but from His. Sanctification is not, as Francis Chan once said, "Running up a down escalator"; sanctification comes when we walk ten more feet and get on the "up" escalator which God designed for us.

True Christian growth is not about doing a lot of hard work to gain these great spiritual disciplines; it comes from letting God guide you in the disciplines that He wishes to teach. Imagine how ineffective it would be to hand a child a pencil, explain in words what to do, and then walk away and expect them to learn to write! No, the effective method involves showing them, talking to them, and standing behind them with your hands on theirs, molding their fingers to the appropriate shape and guiding their pencil on the page. After you have done this for them many times, they may begin practicing on their own.

It is the same with God. You cannot will yourself to have a peaceful spirit. You have to "try softer" and let God impute His righteousness into your heart, allowing it to spill out into peacefulness. It might take years. It might take your whole life. It might happen instantly at the moment you rely on Him instead of your willpower. We don't know when it will happen, but we know from the Bible that God "has given us everything we need for a godly life" (2 Pet 1:3).

Ignore the ridiculous, self-important notion that God needs you to somehow partner with Him to make you holy. God needs you no more than a blizzard needs a snowflake. All He needs is for you to trust and follow Him; what He doesn't need is your list of plans of how to build yourself into a holy person.

Your only chance for spiritual growth comes from an influx of energy from an outside source. Spiritual entropy forbids that you are able to will yourself to being more holy.

– TWELVE –

QUANTUM PHYSICS AND THE WILL

If you too are a sci-fi geek, and have not read anything by Robert Sawyer, then you must immediately rectify this mistake. The Canadian author is not nearly as well known as he should be, for he manages to explore some fascinating concepts in his books. He has an ability to ask truly intriguing questions. What would happen if someone could see the Internet? What would happen if an alien arrived on Earth but (to the horror of scientists) believed in God? What would happen if everyone got a preview of their lives from twenty years in the future? He is excellent at using a single thought experiment to move the plots in his books.

Among his books which I have read, my favorite was definitely *Flashforward*. (It was also the loose inspiration for a television show which, mercifully, was cancelled early in its life. They murdered almost everything I loved about the book when adapting it.)

Flashforward is set in 2009, as the CERN Large Hadron Collider is being used to try and discover the Higgs Boson. (Not a bad prediction: the Higgs Boson was actually discovered in 2012.) During the experiment, a coincidental pulse of neutrinos from a supernova is passing through Earth and the result is that everyone on Earth passes out simultaneously, for two minutes.

During these two minutes, there were no longer any observers on Earth, so per the Copenhagen interpretation (see chapter ten) reality popped back into a state of waveform potentials and no security devices recorded anything. During this two minute blackout, everyone saw a vision of themselves twenty-one years in the future. Those who had no vision eventually realized they were going to die sometime between now and then. This realization creates the central action of the plot, which is philosophical in nature: are the events of the future pre-determined or do we have the free will to change our destiny?

In the book, some argue that the future visions can be proved to be wrong. One famous scientist goes on television and breaks a souvenir from the Smithsonian that he had received as a child and saw in his vision. Obviously, he argues, his future can be changed, since he now no longer owns the souvenir. However, his plan is thwarted when another character mails him a copy of the same souvenir...once again his destiny from his vision can come true. This "fate versus free will" discussion serves as the primary plot catalyst in the book.

The discussion centers around the concepts of how quantum mechanics actually work. Recall from chapter ten that the two most common interpretations of quantum mechanics are the Copenhagen interpretation and the many-worlds interpretation. However, it is wrong to imply that these are the only two; far from it, there are many.

Of these many interpretations, we can basically narrow them down into two broad groups: *deterministic* and *probabilistic*.

Deterministic models argue that there is only one possible outcome in our future. Free will is an illusion, because if we simply knew the laws of nature well enough and understood our starting positions of all particles, and had a perfect computer, we could predict everything that will ever happen.

To put it visually, recall that we Spacelanders can perceive three dimensions of space-time completely: height, width, and depth. So we could imagine taking a three-dimensional snapshot of "now," and we would have a perfect representation of everything that exists.

However, there is a fourth dimension, called time. We cannot perceive of time directly, like we can the three dimensions of space; it seems to us that we are "in" time, being pulled along it. This is because we can only perceive of what we can directly observe. The past is not observable to us, though certain data about past observations are stored in our brains as memories. Meanwhile the future has not yet been perceived by our brains and thus we have no data about those events; the future remains a mystery.

So you might say that the fourth dimension of time is like an *evolution* of our three-dimensional snapshots. It is sort of like those flipbooks you drew as a child: each page had an individual drawing; when flipped, the person appeared to move across the page. The deterministic model is somewhat similar. Each "page" is one snapshot of our three-dimensional universe. Each page has already been written and (if we had good enough computers) the next page could be calculated from the current snapshot and the laws of physics. Nothing you do can change "tomorrow's" flipbook page. You feel as though you have an impact in the world, but in reality you can only make the choices which will bring about the things that tomorrow you will observe. If you could perceive the rules and data well enough, you would be able to predict the future with perfect accuracy.

On the other side of the aisle are the **probabilistic** models of quantum mechanics, which are much more widely accepted by physicists. These models indicate that the future exists as waveforms. In our determinism example, we said each page of the flipbook is a pre-written reality; in a probabilistic model, these pages are not pre-written realities, but instead are a *combination of several possible realities*. So tomorrow there is reality A which is 70% likely and reality B which is 30% likely. It is as if, in your flipbook, there is a 70% chance when I flip the page it will be A and a 30% that it will be B, and it is your observation which forces it to be one or the other.

As we saw in chapter ten, in probabilistic terminology each potential reality is blurred together and called a waveform. These waveforms exist until they are observed, at which point the waveform collapses, and only one reality persists. To use our example from Schrodinger's Cat, this means that both are both equally "real" and "true," and after observation all possibilities but one cease to exist. So tomorrow is not set in stone, as the determinists would say, but rather our future is dependent upon the choices we make and the probabilities of how every quantum particle will travel along its waveform. When observed tomorrow, the waveform will collapse into the reality which is 70% likely or the one which is 30% likely.

Say, for example, that the shirt I choose tomorrow is probabilistically determined. This means that perhaps my favorite plum-colored polo has a 21% chance of being chosen over the other shirts in my closet. Tomorrow, the potential waveform will collapse and one of those realities will be true. But since it has not been observed, no reality exists yet.

(In my case at least, observation really does, literally, determine which shirt I wear. I choose one, and then my wife observes it. If I look ridiculous, she makes me change. Her observation determines my future reality.)

So while the determinists see tomorrow's flipbook page as being already drawn with crisp lines, the probablists would say that tomorrow's flipbook page is a blurry cloud of a thousand sketches competing for the same space on the page; these thousand will collapse into the one true reality as soon as the page is observed.

So there exists a reality in which I wear my plum shirt tomorrow (21% chance), a reality in which I wear my blue shirt (10% chance), a reality in which I go to work naked (0.00001% chance, much to everyone's relief), and so on. All of these events are really, actually occurring; but tomorrow when I wake up, I will observe myself choosing a shirt and the waveform will collapse into what I have chosen, making this reality the only "true" reality, and destroying the other realities. It is not so much that I am "choosing" at this point as it is that I am observing reality and thus forcing it to exist.

So it is not really true free will, in the way that most people think of it, but neither is it completely destiny out of my control, as others would have it. I am not creating the reality out of cloth; tomorrow's reality already exists, and my choice cannot be anything except what I will observe myself choosing tomorrow.

This is perhaps explained best by the main character of *Flashforward*, Lloyd. He says that we have all made all of the choices of our entire lives; we have already drawn our flipbook through a series of choices, but (as creatures who can only perceive the present moment in time) we have not yet "observed" all of the pages. So, he says, we have already made every choice we will ever make, and those choices were free when made, but we have not yet perceived or observed ourselves making those choices.

So if you ask Lloyd, "is the future controlled by destiny or by our choices?," his answer would be, "Yes." Our choices do shape the future and some things do happen probabilistically, but they cannot happen in any way other than the way in which our future selves have already chosen. The fact that we have not yet observed ourselves making the choice does not mean we could make a different choice.

+ + + theology: predestination and free will + + +

It is probably safe to say that, within the Christian fold, no topic has been more divisive throughout history than the argument over freedom of the will. The debate arises due to many passages in Scripture: Exodus 9:12 says that it was God who hardened Pharaoh's heart, leading to the continuation of the plagues; Jeremiah 1:4-5 says that God had appointed Jeremiah as a prophet while still in the womb, seeming to limit the potential of Jeremiah's refusal; Matthew 19:25-26 says that only through God is salvation possible, not through man; John 6:44 says that men can only come to believe in Jesus if God first chose them to do so; John 12:39-40 says that God blinds those who will not be saved so that they cannot follow Him; and Ephesians 1:4-11 states that God predestined believers before the creation of the world.

There are many similar verses, which seem to indicate that it is God, not man, who determines whether we are His followers or not. On the other hand, there are verses which seem to indicate that humans have some freedom in the matter of whether to follow God: Joshua 24:15 says that we can choose whether we serve God or not; John 7:17 says that if anyone wills to follow God, *then* he will learn true doctrine; Acts 2:38 demands that people choose to repent of their sins; and 2 Peter 3:9 says that God's will is not for anyone to perish eternally.

Christians have struggled for centuries to understand such verses. They cannot merely be careless contradictions by differing sources, for often such statements occur within the same book or even a few sentences apart! So clearly there is some concept which ties these together.

Roughly speaking, we may describe the views of Christian theologians as falling into three camps: *Calvinism*, *Arminianism*, and *Lutheranism*.

Calvinism was developed by a number of Reformation preachers, but is so named because of the heavy influence given to it by theologian John Calvin. Calvinism is often described using the five-point TULIP method, where TULIP is an acronym for total depravity, unconditional election, limited atonement, irresistible grace, and perseverance of the saints:

Total depravity: the sin nature of man affects every fiber of our being, and thus we are unable to desire to be saved of our own accord.

Unconditional election: God chose before the foundation of the world whom He would forgive for their sins and, therefore, who would suffer eternally for their sins.

Limited atonement: Christ's substitutionary atonement was limited in that it only applied to those whom God had predestined in "unconditional election"; it has no impact on the righteousness of those whom God did not choose.

Irresistible grace: God's grace is applied effectively to those to whom He chooses to apply it; it cannot be declined by the receiver for this would make their will more powerful than God's.

Perseverance of the saints: because God's will cannot be frustrated by the actions of mankind, those whom He chose will always remain saved; this is sometimes today stated as, "Once saved, always saved."

These are referred to as the "five points of Calvinism," and people often have a very nuanced version of them. For example, someone may identify himself as Reformed theologically (meaning he is somewhat Calvinist), but refer to himself as a "two-point Calvinist" or a "three point Calvinist" or a "four point Calvinist." Generally, when people talk about *"predestination"* in Christian debates, they are referring to unconditional election and irresistible grace: did God choose who would go to heaven and hell before time began, and do humans have the ability to overturn that decision? Thus, someone can be a "three point Calvinist" yet still deny the two points which relate to predestination.

That said, Calvinism in its complete, five-point form does in fact teach that God chose (for reasons we cannot fathom) that some would go to

Heaven and some would go to Hell, and they cannot "choose" something which will change His mind on this.

Calvinism in some form or the other is the dominant feature of modern evangelicalism. Some form of Calvinism (2-point, 3-point, 4-point, or full 5-point) is the stance of many Baptist and evangelical churches, the former head of the Southern Baptist Convention (Al Mohler), the Presbyterian church, and noteworthy pastors and teachers like Mark Driscoll, Tim Keller, R.C. Sproul, John Piper, and Michael Horton.

Arminianism, the primary opposition to Calvinism, comes from the teachings of the Dutch theologian Jacobus Arminius. It takes the opposing view of Calvinism on all five points. This view teaches that man is fallen but still has *prevenient grace* within him to desire God (so depravity is not total); it teaches that election is conditional upon acceptance of Christ; it teaches that atonement is for all; it teaches that man has free will to resist God's will in his life; and it teaches that (logically and resultantly), you can only maintain salvation as long as you maintain belief and penance.

Arminianism is the stance of the United Methodist church, the Free Will Baptists, most Charismatics, and the Church of the Nazarene. General Baptists are a mixture of the two sides: they are generally Arminian in nature but accept at least two points of Calvinism (perseverance of the saints and, generally, total depravity).

A third theology, **Lutheranism,** is often wrongly excluded from the debate. Based upon the teachings of Martin Luther, this is best described in his work, *On the Bondage of the Will.* Luther taught, unlike the Calvinists, that we do have some amount of spiritual will in our lives; we are not robots. However, this willpower is not totally free (as the Arminians would state), but is instead "bound" by our sinful natures and depravity. That is, our will is limited to only being free within certain boundaries: we cannot do things which are surprising to God, nor can we make ourselves holy through our willpower, thus earning salvation or glory before God.

Lutheranism therefore is in between Calvinism and Arminianism in many respects. Luther agrees with Calvin in the total depravity of the will, in the perseverance of the saints, and that God chose before time those who would receive His grace. On the other hand, Lutheranism teaches that Christ died for all men (not just some), as the Calvinists would state. Also, Lutheranism states that though God's grace is initiated without any influence of the individual, nevertheless it is resistible. Thus, you could (and many do) call Luther a "three point Calvinist" or a "three and a half point Calvinist." This is the stance of the Lutheran churches and many non-denominational churches.

I submit to you, however, that such theologies (which are heavily dependent upon understanding how time works) cannot be left in the past centuries where they were developed. This is an area where physics—which studies the nature of time—can inform theologians directly, and we must update any such theology as we understand time better. Indeed, quantum mechanics provides some fascinating influences on the concept of predestination.

If we assume that the deterministic model of quantum physics is correct, then this of course would play directly into the form of Calvinism known as hyper-Calvinism (which implies that men are just robots acting out God's plans): the future is fully set in every detail, and we have no control over it. Feelings of any control are completely an illusion. This explains why God can prophesy about the future with exact accuracy—because He knows everything which will happen, and there is no possibility of doing something that He did not control.

However, things get more intriguing if you follow the Copenhagen interpretation, or some other interpretation of the probabilistic model. As you will recall, this model indicates that our future is not set, but exists as a series of potential realities. So at first glance, one might find this analogous to Arminianism: we can choose which of the potential paths we follow in life, with complete freedom. Some paths are more likely than others, true, but we still have the choice. This has profound negative theological implications, though: if God were to prophesy about such a future, He presumably would have to stay pretty vague: He could not truly say, "such and such will turn out to be saved," or "so and so would end up a prophet"; rather, He would have to say, "such and such *is likely* to turn out to be saved," or "so and so *would likely* end up a prophet."

What is interesting, however, is that the Copenhagen interpretation says something completely different. It says that all possible future realities really exist, but only until they are observed. This would thus go well with Arminianism...*but only if there was no God*. For if there is One who has observed the future, and prophesied about the future, then the potential waveforms would collapse. Only the reality which God observed would still remain valid.

Recall from chapter one that God is an extra-dimensional being, at least as great as the four dimensional space-time He has created for us to live within. As a result, He must be capable of seeing all of time simultaneously, just as we can see "up/down," "left/right," and "in/out" simultaneously. The Bible is quite clear that God observes us past, present, and future. He prophesies about things to come, sends visions to His people, and talks about the past. That is, God is observing our timeline in all directions.

What would be the result of this, according to quantum physics? Well, the waveform of all potential futures would collapse into one reality. On every "page" of your flipbook, your infinite 'free will' choices would be collapsed into one reality, the one which God observed. No longer do you have truly free will, in the way we think of it: for you cannot choose something that He did not already observe.

So we see then that, following the logic of quantum physics, the question, "Does God choose who goes to Hell or do we choose?" is really a false dichotomy. The question is nonsense, for it does not describe the reality of how the universe works. It is not that God chose one small portion of people to go to Heaven and the rest He chose to go to Hell. That is, He did not draw every page of the flipbook for us and we had to follow it. But neither is it "free will," in that you can draw whatever you want on the pages of time, and God is just along for the ride, with no sovereign power.

Rather, quantum physics implies that reality is more like this: God created mankind and, because of either our acceptance or rejection of Him, there are an infinite number of potential realities. In some I go to Hell and in others I do not; in some my wife goes to Hell and in others she does not, etc. The waveform of all of our futures existed in all of its possible forms before any of us were born. From God's perspective (being outside of time), He could view all possible realities which any of our free choices would make. And then, God observed this timeline: He chose one of those combinations waveforms (presumably the one which led to His sovereign purpose), and observed it. As God, He chose the narrative that our flipbook would possess. Because of this observation, all other potential realities collapsed into non-existence.

As Lloyd says in *Flashforward*, we have already made all of our choices, but we simply have not yet experienced making them. Do you have free will? Yes and no. Every choice you make is made freely; however, of all the possible combinations of realities, God chose one to be true, and so the choices you make are the ones which He already observed you making in this timeline. Did God predestine some to Hell and some to Heaven? Yes and no. We all make our choices freely, but of the infinite possible realities that this could create, God chose this one (in which certain people will end up in Hell) to be the "true" reality. So in one way, we individuals are responsible and accountable for our choices in this reality for we truly did choose them; yet in another way God is the sovereign power responsible because He is the one who chose which of the infinite combination of realities would become the True reality.

So in a very real way, we are choosing what we choose freely; we are drawing our flipbook each day. But God choose this one reality out of all of the possible futures which could have existed, and said, "This is the one which will become true and really happen." So you make your daily choices freely...but the other paths which you could have taken have already collapsed because God observed this path. You can choose what you wish: but you cannot choose something which will surprise God, as He has already observed your choice, and chosen this particular timeline of choices out of the infinite alternative timelines of choices you would have made.

So when the Bible says (as Jesus does in John 15:16), that we choose Him only after He chooses us, we see in quantum mechanics a very intriguing explanation describing how we are choosing and yet He already chose. Every choice we make would create an infinite number of potential futures: God chose the one which is His sovereign plan, and thus every choice we make today—though made "freely"—are bound by the choice of timeline which He made. We cannot choose something different from the "us" that He chose to be true.

So in a way, yes, God chose to send some people to Hell and others to go to Heaven. But in another very real way, it was their own choice; God did not force them to choose Hell, but He did choose this "timeline" (in which some of us have chosen Him and some have not) to become the true timeline. So while every choice you are making is completely free for you to make, you will only be making them in the way He observed before He chose this reality to become true.

It is as if you drew a million flipbooks for your life, each of them truly and freely drawn by you, and then God chose which flipbook would come true. You truly drew it and made those choices, but He is the one who made it become reality. We do not know how God chose which flipbook to make reality; it was His right as sovereign Creator to choose the one He preferred. Perhaps it is the one with the most saved; perhaps the one with the least harm; perhaps one of a hundred other possibilities, we do not know.

What we do know is that even though we had freedom when drawing our flipbook, now that one reality has been chosen our wills are bound, much like Luther stated. We do have some freedom of will: but we do not have the freedom to choose something which God does not expect, or which is different from the future which He chose to observe. When He observed the waveforms, His sovereign choice led to all of the infinite possible choices we could make in life collapsing into one true reality.

So do you have free will? Yes, and no. The waveform of reality was one of an infinite number of possibilities, in some of which you rejected Him and in some of which you accepted Him. He could have chosen any of these to make real. In His sovereign authority He chose one of these timelines to be reality and ultimately true. So in a very real way, you chose Him only because He chose you: in many other potential realities you rejected Him, but those were not the realities which remained after His divine Observation.

We freely made all of our choices along our life's path, but once God chose this reality and collapsed the waveform, we no longer have freedom to deny Him and jump to another path. They no longer exist. We choose...but our willpower is bound to the path which He observed and chose to make reality.

– THIRTEEN –

LOST, FIREFLY AND THE MAGISTERIUM

On September 22, 2004, my wife and I sat down to watch TV. We had no real plans about what to watch, but there was a new show starting which was made by the guy who did *Alias*, so we figured we would check it out. Almost immediately, a dramatic plane crash occurs. The plane crashing into the island was interesting; but when we heard the Monster in the forest, we were hooked. From that point on, my wife and I watched every single episode of *Lost*, one of the geekiest mainstream shows of all time.

Lost was an incredible and ambitious series, and expected its viewers to figure things out on their own rather than having the answers clearly explained by the show. As the series went on, the mysteries grew more and more deep and complex. At the end of the first episode, the only real mysteries were, "What is the monster in the woods" and "Why does John Locke look so scary?" By the end of the sixth season, many of its millions of viewers were completely and utterly confused by its deep mysteries.

In the first season, a plane crash strands the "castaways," as they were called, on an unknown tropical island in the Pacific. Some sort of Monster roams the forest, and a number of unexplainable events occur: they are attacked by a polar bear, hear a creepy French recording broadcasting from the island on a loop for sixteen years, meet a wild-eyed woman named Rousseau who speaks of a sickness on the island, and find a mysterious metal hatch buried in the ground.

In the second season, the natives on the island (The Others) become a major part of the plot, and the two main leaders of the survivors (Jack and John Locke) begin battling for supremacy. The Hatch is explored and found to be a research site built by a mysterious organization called the Dharma Initiative.

In the third season, the history of The Others begins to unfold and a former recruit of Dharma joins the castaways. The battle between the castaways and The Others escalates into more violence, and even more mysteries unfold.

In the fourth season, the survivors figure out a way off the island, and we begin to see (through scenes set in the future) a bit of the lives of the Oceanic Six, who will escape the island. A magical wheel is discovered beneath the island to keep it safe, and when the wheel is turned the island is moved in time and space.

In the fifth season, the survivors still left on the now time-jumping island experience a number of timelines before settling in 1974, when the Dharma Initiative first arrived on the island. The survivors who escaped are shown in the original timeline where they live three years before deciding to return to the island; when they do, their plane crashes and some wake up in 1977 (with the time-jumping survivors) while others wake up in 2007.

In the sixth and final season, the survivors are fighting the Monster (now known as the Man in Black), while a parallel universe in which the original flight never crashed is also shown. Throughout the season it is revealed that the island is a mystical place which provides the source of life on Earth, and thus needs protecting. A new protector is chosen for the island from among the castaways, the Monster is defeated, and it is revealed that the parallel universe was a form of limbo where those who died on the island were waiting to be reunited to the other castaways. At the end of the show the dead castaways move on to the afterlife together.

Clear and straightforward to follow, right?

Lost was a fascinating show, brilliantly written and well-acted. It had mysteries within mysteries within mysteries. A typical episode would answer one mystery and ask three or four more. The depth and detail of the show was staggering. To give some idea of the detailed geekiness inspired by the show, the Wikipedia articles about Lost, its six seasons, and its mythology would be about 250 pages in book form! This excludes the long articles on character biographies and episode-by-episode summaries.

As great as the series is for those who watch it on DVD now, it was something far greater to those of us watching the mysteries unfold. Every single week, after the show aired, a good portion of my next day was spent on

Television Without Pity (TWOP), an internet forum which had some extremely good observers. Reading TWOP was very, very helpful to understanding the show. It was not necessary, for the main plot points were understandable to anyone who was a consistent viewer; but it was very helpful. On the TWOP boards, my wife and I discovered all kinds of minor things we had missed— references to obscure books or music, contextual clues we didn't catch, clarifications of confusing speeches, etc.

Lost was also one of the first shows to use interactive tie-ins outside of the main show to provide extra information for its viewers. *The Lost Experience*, a book called *Bad Twin*, special videos shown at Comic-Con, and other information given outside of the primary show added a tremendous amount of depth to some of the minor characters and background institutions, making the overall show's world feel even more immersive.

Lost not only embraced, but *required*, its viewers to be geeks and really think through the series in detail if they wished to understand everything which was going on. This in turn made the show a blast to watch.

Lost is not the only series to benefit from the collaboration of geeks and the use of information outside the main series to help add depth. *Dr. Horrible's Sing Along Blog*, starring Neil Patrick Harris and written by geek icon Joss Whedon, tells the story of an aspiring super-villain (Dr. Horrible) who battles an obnoxious hero (Captain Hammer), largely over a girl. The musical miniseries shows Dr. Horrible eventually becoming the super-villain he desires, but only after ironically losing the thing he most wanted in the world. Dr. Horrible was made even better by a series of comics released afterward (written by Zack Whedon, Joss' brother). Like the Lost tie-ins, these comics helped clarify some of the motivations and gave more context to the characters, giving more depth to some of the actions we saw on the screen.

The same is true of Whedon's other series, and probably my favorite television series of all time, *Firefly*. Firefly was a sort of science fiction space-western, following the crew of a firefly-class smuggling vessel named *Serenity* as it went on a series of adventures. Much like Star Wars, the smugglers stayed on the outskirts of an oppressive empire, with the main captain being a Han Solo-like lovably brash hothead who fought for the rebellion. In Firefly, the crew takes on a few strange tag-a-longs who all seem to be on the run—a deeply religious preacher named Shepherd Book, a doctor named Simon Tam, and Simon's crazy sister River.

The incredible series was cancelled before it could ever fully hit its stride, but the fan outcry led to the movie *Serenity*, which answered most of the major open mysteries. One mystery throughout the series, which was not answered in the movie, involved the background of Shepherd Book. We know that the Shepherd is not all he seems; in one episode Book uses an Alliance access code and an officer says mysteriously that he isn't a Shepherd. He is a deadly shot, too. In one episode he picks up a gun as a battle nears. When it is pointed out that the Bible is pretty specific about not killing others, Shepherd replies: "Quite specific. It is, however, somewhat fuzzier on the subject of kneecaps." This seemingly peaceful preacher then goes on an impressive shooting display. The intriguing mystery of his past led to many discussions among fans, even though it was not actually necessary to notice these things in order follow the show's primary plot. After the movie, Zack Whedon wrote a comic book which explained Shepherd's history, helping to clear up these issues.

This process of using outside tie-ins and relying on the Internet discussions of geeks adds great flavor to a series. In none of these instances was it necessary to participate in the tie-ins in order to understand the primary themes and plot of the series. If you did so, however, you found a greater depth of appreciation for the source material, more clarity on questionable issues, and the series made more sense. The tie-ins were not necessary, but were helpful.

+ + + theology: Scripture + + +

In chapter nine, we briefly discussed the five solas of the Reformation, and noted that the actual key difference was the understanding of *sola scriptura*; whatever you believe about the Old and New Testaments, and how to interpret them, will greatly affect your theological views.

When it comes to Scripture, there are really three major questions: (1) can we trust that the Bible we have today is a fair representation of the

Bible as originally written; (2) to what extent is the Bible accurate; and (3) do we require the Magisterium to interpret it (as per Catholic theology) or can we interpret it ourselves (as per Protestant theology)?

Let us treat each of these individually.

The transmission of the Scripture

The topic of Biblical reliability and transmission is a massive topic which I cannot possibly cover in detail here, but I will say a few basic things.

The Old Testament was written over a period stretching from Moses (c. 1500 BC) to Malachi (c. 400 BC), and translated into the Greek Septuagint around 250 BC. This was the most common version of the Old Testament. The Jewish authors took the text so seriously that, when copying or translating, if they made a mistake with even a single accent mark they would burn the entire copy, so as to ensure that the error did not propagate. The original copies of the Old Testament (called the *autographs*) have been lost to time, but we have many ancient manuscript copies (the Dead Sea Scrolls, the Geniza Fragments, the Aleppo Codex, etc.).

The New Testament writings were authored between 40 and 100 AD, and we have thousands of manuscript copies of it, dating as early as 125 AD with the p-52 manuscript. The Codex Sinaiticus, dating from 350 AD, contains the entire New Testament and almost the entire Old Testament. Many early Christians wrote amazing works from the time of Christ which survived until now, but only those written by the apostles or the apostles' students were considered canonical and accepted as New Testament scripture.

To gain an understanding of why we can trust that the Bible we have today is a reliable copy of the original autograph, we need only compare it to other ancient works which historians trust implicitly.

Plato wrote about 400 BC, and we have 7 manuscripts of his work, with the earliest dating from 900 AD (1,300 years after it was written). Tacitus wrote about 100 AD, and we have 20 manuscripts with the earliest dating from 1100 AD (1,000 years after). Homer's *Iliad* (the best-transmitted ancient document except for the Bible) was written about 900 BC, and we have 643 manuscripts dating as early as 400 BC (500 years after the writing).

The New Testament? We have over 24,000 manuscripts, dating as early as 125 AD...some parts only 25-50 years after the original autograph was written. Most impressively, these 24,000 manuscripts agree with each other on over 99.5% of textual details (the other 0.5% consisting mostly of spelling and word order variations).

Why the difference? Even key administrative documents of the mighty Roman Empire are not as well preserved as the New Testament. The early Christians were passionate about protecting the Scripture. Whenever a letter from an apostle was sent to a church, it was copied several times and sent to every other church in the region, generally using the same intense copying methods used by the Jews. Later, after the Fall of Rome, the only institution which had the power to maintain learning and libraries were the Orthodox and Catholic Churches, so they set their monks to copying the Bible over and over and over again.

So we can have strong confidence that the New Testament we hold today is 99.5% accurate to the original autograph written by the apostles. (For more information, see the works by Deem, Holding, and Metzger cited in the bibliography.)

Scriptural Inspiration

So we can be confident that the passages we read are reliably accurate transmissions of what the apostles originally wrote. But why should we trust what the apostles had to say? This is a topic called Scriptural inspiration, and again this is too large a topic to cover in one-third of one chapter. However, it is important to have a general overview of how inspiration works.

In Kaufmann Kohler's *Jewish Theology*, he discusses the manner in which the ancient Jews viewed Scripture:

"Where [divine inspiration] is felt, it bursts forth as from a higher world, creating for itself its proper organs and forms. The rabbis portray God as saying to Israel, 'Not I in My higher realm, but you with your human needs fix the form, the measure, the time, and the mode of expression for that which is divine."

The ancient Jews saw the Scripture (which to them was comprised of the *Torah* of Moses and the wisdom and prophetic writings which make up the rest of our Old Testament) as divinely inspired by God but recorded in human voices and with human cultural viewpoints. So God inspired Moses to write the *Torah*, but Moses spoke in his own voice and word choice when doing the writing. Thus, David the poet wrote songs and poetry; Solomon the philosopher wrote proverbs; Jeremiah (who was likely depressed) wrote sad lamentations; etc. In order to understand the Scripture, we need to understand both the culture of the human writer as well as the inspiration of God.

Paul, who saw the inspiration the same way, tells us why God inspires Biblical writings in 2 Timothy 3:15-17:

"[F]rom childhood you have been acquainted with the sacred writings, which are able to make you wise for salvation through faith in Christ Jesus. All Scripture is breathed out by God and profitable for teaching, for reproof, for correction, and for training in righteousness, that the man of God may be complete, equipped for every good work."

In this passage Paul says not only that the Scriptures are "God-breathed" or divinely inspired, but tells us why God does the inspiring: (1) to bring you to saving faith in Christ, and (2) to equip you for doing good works.

Because the Scriptures were seen as inspired by God, the ancient Jews treated them very seriously. Every accent mark was considered important (Matt 5:18). The shape of the letters was analyzed for hidden information. They treated the text with such sobriety because, although men recorded the words inspired by God, it was still seen as "God's word," and to change or alter it was considered a grave sin. The early creeds of Christianity applied the same divine inspiration to the writings of the apostles in the New Testament.

As you begin to read various writers and their statements on Biblical authority, what you will find is that some people use the same terms in different ways: the term "inerrancy," for example, means different things to different people. This lack of consistency results in theological arguments in which both sides are talking past each other, failing to see that they are actually debating different things due to semantical variances.

Therefore, let us begin by defining how I shall use the terms. Non-Christians see the Bible as either being a fairy tale or being a mythology which simply "contains some truth." But Christians have always had a different view. Generally speaking, the views of Christianity on Biblical inspiration can be divided into three categories: *infallibility*, *inerrancy*, and *immutability*.

Infallibility is the view that God inspired the Bible to tell His Story and to accomplish the purposes as described by Paul in 2Timothy 3 (to lead men to salvation and to equip men to do good works). Infallibility says the Bible is completely without error in these areas. So regarding matters of doctrine and faith, the Bible is completely trustworthy and wholly without mistake. But other errors are completely possible, so the science or history as recorded in the Bible may be flawed based upon the people whom God inspired. The infallibility view of Scripture is that God inspired it and for the purposes of salvation and righteous living it is infallible, but in other matters it is a reflection of the human author's view of the world, not God's.

Inerrancy is the view that there is no error at all in the Bible, though it assumes four conditions:

The Bible is inerrant in its original autograph. The original copies of the books, as penned by the authors whom God inspired, were inerrant. Translation errors, copying errors, misquotes, etc., are possible in later copies, so whenever possible try and get to the most original source.

The Bible is inerrant in its original language. The inerrancy view acknowledges that God inspired people who spoke a certain language (e.g., Hebrew, Greek, Aramaic) and since human languages are limited this inherently limits some of what can be said. For example, the Hebrews did not have words for all modern phyla of animals. They used the word *'owph* for all flying creatures; thus the Bible identifies bats as *'owph*, which translators then (wrongly) render as birds. Skeptics see this as a Biblical inaccuracy, when in fact it is not; there being no Hebrew word for "flying mammal," God's inspiration of course must fit within the boundaries of the language within which it is written. So calling a bat an *'owph* is not an error in the text, simply a limitation of the Hebrew language at the time of writing.

The Bible is inerrant in its original context. Inerrantists are sometimes called 'literalists', which is untrue. Inerrantists do not believe the entire Bible is to be taken literally, but must be read within its context. Inerrantists believe the entire Bible is without error, but acknowledge that poetry or symbolism states its truths differently than historical narratives or scientific statements. If I say "the sun rose today," I do not literally mean that the sun left the ground and moved through the sky; this is a common-place phrase which is used to communicate that a new day has begun. Likewise, the context is key to understanding the Bible when applying any concept of inerrancy.

The Bible is inerrant in its original scope. Inerrantists do not claim that the Bible is without error beyond the scope of the claims that it makes. For example, Matthew 4 records Satan as promising Jesus authority over the world; the inerrantist only believes that the Bible is accurately reporting what Satan says, not accurately reporting that Satan had such authority. If a census reports that there are 10,000 people, this does not mean that there really were 10,000 people, merely that the census *reported* 10,000 people. Biblical characters are allowed to make mistakes, the Scripture is inerrant in recording what they said (right or wrong).

The other view of Scripture, sometimes wrongly mixed up with inerrancy, is what I call **immutability**. Immutability is sort of like inerrancy on steroids: it says that the Bible is *unchangeably* inerrant. That is, the context is always clear and straightforward at all times (regardless of culture), and God protects His word from transcription errors, textual mistakes, or limitations in language. In order to hold this position logically you must limit the scope somewhat: obviously Thomas Jefferson's razor-bladed Bible and the KJV are mutually-exclusive. So immutability demands the person to choose one particular textual lineage (e.g., "everything deriving from the Masoretic texts") or one particular translation (e.g., "King James Version") as being specially protected by God. The immutabilists would tend to reject the conditions of the inerrantists.

All three views (infallibility, inerrancy, and immutability) have been held by Christians and are valid positions for the Christian thinker. We can all agree that the texts have been accurately transmitted to us; and after reviewing these versions of inspiration you can determine whether you are an infallibilist, an inerrantist, or an immutabilist.

The Magisterium

Now that we have a solid basis of trust in the Scripture, we come to the primary question raised by the Reformers: can we individuals, led by the Holy Spirit, reliably interpret the Scriptures ourselves or do we need a group of wise advisors (such as the Catholic Magisterium) to tell us how to interpret it?

This concept—*sola scriptura*—was really the primary "super-principle" upon which the other four *solas* rest. (And, full disclosure, it is this theological topic which led me to leave the Roman Catholic Church, even though I still have great respect for my Roman brethren.)

In the end, it was technology which destroyed the need for a Magisterium to interpret Scripture for us. During the Dark Ages, when the vast majority of the populace was uneducated, the Bibles were hand-copied, in Latin, and quite expensive to own. It was not at all unusual for an entire region to have no copy of the Bible (including the priests). In such a time, the only hope for ensuring proper doctrine was for a group of highly-educated Christians to serve as the priesthood and teach the others.

This unfortunately also resulted in an inordinate amount of power being focused on a very few people, and even Catholic historians admit that the Middle Ages were a black eye for the Roman Church. John Wycliffe, an English theologian and preacher, began to try and give the Bible back to the layperson by translating the Bible into common English in 1382, and was a vocal opponent of the Catholic Church's political activities (which he saw as corrupting their interpretations of proper Christian doctrine). Wycliffe died from a stroke in 1384, but his teachings and Bible were beginning to become widespread and eventually, in 1428, a Catholic council declared him a heretic. They burned his books, and at the command of Pope Martin V, he was posthumously excommunicated. His body was dug up from its grave and burned, and his ashes scattered in a river.

In 1439, Johannes Gutenberg invented the printing press and by 1450 it was in full operation. In 1455, Gutenberg began printing Bibles, which (though still costing about three years' salary) were far cheaper and more easily made than a hand-copied Bible, which might take a year and tenfold the price to complete. When Martin Luther launched the Protestant Reformation in 1517, the printing press was a major reason for his success. He wrote his debates in the common language and utilized the mass-production methods of the printing press, placing copies of his tracts in the hands of merchants who would spread it all around the countryside. The Catholic Church continued to write their responses in archaic Latin and share it only with the priests; as such, Luther was able to capture the hearts of the populace. In the end, the embracing of new technology and the translation of the Bible and commentaries into the common tongue led to a sort of populist religious movement, and it is largely due to this that the Reformation was so incredibly effective.

Today, thanks to further technological innovation, we are in an even better situation. Anyone can access, for free, incredible Bible study websites or apps on our smartphones; we can read the Bible in its original languages, which are then hyperlinked to concordances and commentaries where we can see what theologians and translation experts think about the passage. We can compare any number of texts and translations to each other. It is no exaggeration to say that the common, uneducated layperson of today can access more deep and varied theological thought and translational accuracy than even the greatest theologians of three centuries ago.

It is largely for that reason that I, as a geek, have a big problem with the Magisterium approach to Scripture. With access to the Scriptures in their original languages and the ability to do complex Bible analysis on our own, we no longer need someone to explain it to us. Perhaps we never did; after all, Deuteronomy says,

"For this commandment that I command you today is not too hard for you, neither is it far off. It is not in heaven, that you should say, 'Who will ascend to heaven for us and bring it to us, that we may hear it and do it?' Neither is it beyond the sea, that you should say, 'Who will go over the sea for us and bring it to us, that we may hear it and do it?' But the word is very near you. It is in your mouth and in your heart, so that you can do it." (Deut 30:11-14)

We geeks did not actually have to participate in the Lost tie-ins or read the message boards or buy the Whedon comics in order to understand the basic plots of our shows. In the same way, any lay-reader who reads the Scriptures can come away understanding what the Bible says about its key theme—belief in the need for salvation by Christ and the teaching necessary to good works (2 Tim 3:15-17). We do not need a priesthood of experts explaining it to us; the key storyline of the story of the Bible, as written by its Author, is clear to any reader.

This is not to say, of course, that studying extra-Biblical works or seeking the advice of wise scholars is not valuable. It is very valuable, and I highly recommend it. Just as reading the Whedon comics helped us understand Dr. Horrible better, and participating in the TWOP message boards helped me see things that I missed in Lost, so too does studying extra-Biblical sources help clarify Scripture. We live in a time where we are blessed to have access to the writings of Clement and Ignatius and Justin Martyr and Polycarp—men who knew the apostles, trained under the apostles, and can help us better understand the text of the Bible. Likewise, studying concordances and theological works and commentaries helps us gain a much better, deeper, richer understanding of the Scripture.

Sola scriptura does not mean you should ignore the input of other thinkers. Every day, for example, my Google reader pulls from a series of brilliant blog authors from every corner of Christianity—Anglican, Baptist, Catholic, Episcopal, Lutheran, Methodist, Orthodox, and Presbyterian—and I read them all. All have great insight into better understanding the Scriptures. I highly encourage you to read what the early church fathers wrote, and what believers from all sides of Christianity say about a text. It will add a richness and depth and beauty to your faith. I also regularly consult my copy of *Dictionary of Early Christian Beliefs*, and read early Christian writings and histories. These acts illuminate the Scriptural text and give it a richer theological understanding.

What *sola scriptura* does mean is that studying these extra-Biblical sources is not *necessary* in order to understand the key themes of the Bible. A complete layperson, led by the Holy Spirit, can understand all of the fundamentals of the Gospel simply from reading the Bible. He can come to conclude all of the twenty-five key doctrines of Christianity (outlined in chapter fourteen) simply from reading the Bible for himself. He does not need a priesthood to come and explain to him how to interpret it, and when someone tells an interpretation to him which does not fit within the canon of Scripture, he has the complete right to reject such an opinion.

This is the basis of *sola scriptura*. It is the populist movement of the faith, the returning of the power of interpretation to the people, rather than the priesthood. It is the freedom to simply read the Story as written or to read all of the tie-ins for an even better and richer understanding.

– FOURTEEN –

ATOMIC STRUCTURE AND IONIC HERESY

As I mentioned before, I was always more of a physics and mathematics geek than any other science. Biology, chemistry, and geology were okay, but it was in physics and mathematics that I found myself fascinated and excited. So even when it comes to topics which are generally understood through the eyes of another discipline, I tend to see them as a physicist more than anything else. For example, when I discuss biology I care little about taxonomic memorization and fossil records and genomic coding; on the other hand I find myself engrossed with discussions of population statistical probabilities, mathematical difficulties for species variation, and biomechanics. In the same way, I found atomic theory far more interesting from a physics standpoint than a chemistry standpoint.

Scientists and philosophers long believed that there was some fundamental building block which was used (either by nature or God) to build up the rest of the universe; a sort of miniature LEGO which could be combined with other miniature LEGOs to create everything around us. This was called an "atom," meaning that it could not be subdivided (though of course, now we know that the thing we ended up naming the "atom" is divisible into smaller things). However, due to the incredibly small size of the atom most of the research about it must be indirect.

By the start of the twentieth century, scientists knew about the existence of atoms and some of how they reacted in various situations. Electrons were also known to exist in the atom and known to be of negative charge, yet the overall charge of the atom remained neutral. Thus physicists and chemists began to develop models to attempt to describe what the atom looked like and explain all of these data.

At the turn of the century, J.J. Thomson had the most popular model of the atom, often compared to plum pudding. The atom was seen as a fluid of positive charge, with electrons sort of floating in it. Thus the overall atom remained neutral while the electrons were negative. In 1911, Ernest

Rutherford's laboratory tested the theory and ruled it out, as they found by scattering particles through gold foil that the particles moved at angles which could only be produced if the positive charge of the atom was very tightly concentrated in a small area.

In 1913, Niels Bohr (also working for Rutherford) proposed the model of that atom that we all learned in school: like a miniature solar system, the nucleus (composed of positively-charge protons and uncharged neutrons) were bound at the center of the atom, with the negatively-charged electrons orbiting around it. From a classical physics standpoint, this model intuitively makes sense: an electron with a negative charge $-e$ traveling in a circular orbit around a nucleus composed of a positive charge would have an inward attraction due to the opposite charges, which is counteracted by the centripetal acceleration of its circular motion, resulting in a stable orbit. (In other words, the electrical attraction between the electron and proton work similarly to the gravitational attraction between a planet and star in classical mechanics). Thus there is an attractive electrical force of kNe^2/r^2, where k is the Coulomb constant, N is the number of protons, e is the electrical charge, and r is the atomic radius.

Bohr's model quickly spread because it was both useful and predictable; however, even early on it was well understood by physicists that Bohr's model was not strictly true. At first blush, it seems as though the Coloumb attractive force would provide the sufficient energy needed to maintain an orbit; however, the electron upon accelerating in the circle would naturally radiate electromagnetic energy, thus losing the required energy to resist the attraction to the proton. The atom would quickly become electromagnetically unstable and collapse. With some work, Bohr was able to add some assumptions which would mathematically stabilize the atom; however, these were theoretical constructs only and without experimental or theoretical justification. To put it bluntly, they were fudge factors to make the math match the experiment. There was simply no reason for them; and as Ockham's Razor has long taught scientists, we should not needlessly add assumptions.

Quantum mechanics came along and resolved these difficulties, in ways which I will not discuss, lest I begin to reveal my ignorance. Instead, suffice it to say that Bohr's nice circular orbits for electrons were replaced with electron probability clouds, and his calculations were found to be specific solutions of the wave potentials for electrons. And thus the Bohr model is a useful (though slightly inaccurate) approximation of reality, much like Newtonian gravity.

So the Bohr model you learned in chemistry was more or less accurate: each atom is comprised of a number of positively-charged protons and an equal number of negatively-charged electrons, for a net zero charge. Additional mass is added to the nucleus by neutrons. The electrons, being negatively charged, are attracted to the nucleus but repelled by other electrons, and spin around the nuclear center of the atom. They spin at various energy levels, called shells; the closer the shell the more stably the electron orbits the nucleus.

But frequently, this attraction to the center is interrupted by other situations. Recall from our discussions of entropy that nature always prefers a lower-energy state to a higher-energy state; sometimes engineers will say that all things take the "path of least resistance." Often in nature, it takes less energy for an atom to gain or lose an electron in its outer shell than to retain its natural, stable atomic form. Sodium, for example, has eleven electrons, with only one in its valence (outer) shell; the other ten electrons are "tighter" to the nucleus. Thus it is quite easy for the extra electron to be ripped away from sodium, if it requires less energy to rip it away than it does to retain its position.

When an atom gains or loses an electron, it is no longer an atom; it is called an *ion*. A cation is an atom which has lost electrons and now has a net positive charge; an anion is an atom which has gained electrons and now has a net negative charge.

Ions are everywhere in nature, and are extremely useful. But at its core, one can see ions as a distortion of the natural state of things: it is the loss (cation) or gain (anion) of electrons, which fundamentally changes the atom, allowing it to bond to new things, or be manipulated in new ways.

+ + + theology: heresy + + +

C.S. Lewis once said, "Christianity, if false, is of no importance, and if true is of infinite importance. The only thing it cannot be is moderately important." He of course is correct: if Christianity is true, and if we teach Christianity incorrectly, then we run the risk of excluding others or ourselves from the kingdom of God. Jesus said as much to the Pharisees (Matt 23:13), and perhaps not coincidentally much of the New Testament discusses the teaching of proper doctrine (Matt 1:9, Matt 5-7, Matt 15:1-9, Acts 20:28-31, Rom 16:17, 2 Pet 2; 1 Tim 1:3-4; Tit 1:9, many more).

Matthew 18:6 says that teachers would be better off drowned than to have misled people about Him, and James (Jesus' brother) says that most people should avoid being teachers due to the harsher judgment teachers will receive (Jam 3:1). Revelation 22:18 warns against adding to the words of the Bible. Even after the apostles, a great deal of concern existed for teaching proper theology; one of the earliest Christian writers, Irenaeus, wrote a multi-volume work titled *Against Heresies* (a *heresy* being any un-orthodox teaching which has the potential to divide the body of Christ due to its falsity).

I like to picture Christian philosophy as an atom. At the center of the atom, providing both the energy source and the only mass of any importance, is the Triune God. He is the central "proton" of the faith, and His teachings and true nature must be the primary focus of our belief system. Everything we do should orbit around Him. Closely connected with Him are the teachings in Holy Scripture; these are like the neutrons of Christian philosophy, adding no additional power but helping add mass to, and thus draw attention toward, God. Thus one might consider God as the proton of our theology, and Scripture as the neutron; together they form the nucleus around which all proper teaching should orbit.

In this analogy, our theologies are like electrons orbiting around the nucleus. In the natural state, our theologies must be held into their proper place by their attraction to God and Scripture. Just as physicists discovered with electrons, theologies often are not completely and perfectly neat orbits; rather, there is some "cloudiness" to many theologies, and we must allow each other grace to disagree on non-essential doctrines.

Recall that different electrons are in different shells in an atom: some are more closely bonded to the neutron, and others are further away. Such it is with theology as well. As long as a theology is centrally orbiting Christ, then it is okay to differ from other theologies. Some are undoubtedly closer to Christ than others; that is, some are safely within stable "inner shells" of theology, while others float dangerously around in the valence shell, barely connected to Christian orthodoxy, in danger of being ripped away altogether.

A heresy, then, is like an ion in atomic theory. Just as an ion either sees something new added into the atom (in the case of an anion) or something which should be there stripped away (in the case of a cation), so too is heresy the acceptance of the bulk of Christianity with a slight perversion which fundamentally changes the nature of the teaching.

An *anion heresy* is a teaching which adds to orthodox Christianity in such a way that it can no longer retain its coherent narrative and Jesus-shaped theology. A good example is the teaching of the Latter-Day Saints, more commonly called the Mormon Church. The Mormons consider themselves Christians, while no orthodox Christians agree. Why? Because the Mormons accept everything in the Christian Scriptures, but add on a few more electrons (the Book of Mormon and the teachings of their church Prophets), thus fundamentally changing the nature of the atomic structure of the Christian theology. As with any anion, they become more negatively-charged than was designed: that is, the positive charge of Jesus is overshadowed by the negative charge of what has been added (the Mormon-specific doctrines).

A *cation heresy* is a teaching which subtracts from Scripture in such a way that it fundamentally changes orthodoxy of the faith. One good modern example are the Unitarians, who deny the Trinity and Godhood of Christ, as well as denying doctrines such as sin nature and Biblical accuracy. (Some, but not all, also deny that Christianity is a necessary for salvation whatsoever.) They still call themselves Christians, but are well outside of the orthodoxy of Christian faith.

So while it is both intriguing and important for us to try and determine what we believe, we must always be wary that we are neither adding to, nor taking away from, the teachings of Scripture about God. Some things are clearly stated and cannot be removed; some things are left mysterious and we must be wary of our intellectualized attempts to "explain" them, for often this ends up adding to the Gospel.

Instead, we should seek what I call an Atomic Theology: a basic, fundamental, natural theology which defines our faith. It is the simple faith in this theology which allows God's grace to justify us, sanctify us, and grant us eternal life. But how do we know what makes up such a theology?

Thankfully, the early Christians did most of this work for us. Whenever a major doctrinal dispute arose in the early church, the leaders of Christianity called councils together to help define exactly what the apostles had taught them. These were called Ecumenical Councils, and the first several were quite productive at lining out the basics of Christian theology. The councils of Jerusalem (50 AD), Nicaea (325), Ephesus (431), and Chalcedon (451) well defined and clarified Christian doctrine prior to the fall of Rome. After that point, councils argued increasingly political points and philosophies, and thus I exclude these later councils from being a "requirement" of the faith.

I would argue that the creeds of these four councils, as well as the early creed known as the Apostle's Creed, provide twenty-five key statements which define the proper boundaries of Christian theology. If you accept all twenty-five statements, and really believe them in your heart and are committed to serving Christ because of them, then you are a Christian. If you do not believe in these, then you are not a Christian. Adding to them, or subtracting from them, risks heresy.

Therefore, in summarizing these creeds I present the Atomic Theology of Christianity:

1. We believe that all people (Jew or Gentile, male or female, slave or free) can be followers of Christ.

2. We believe that Gentiles are not bound by the Mosaic Law.

3. We believe in God, the Father Almighty.

4. We believe that God created all things, visible or invisible.

5. We believe that Jesus Christ, the Lord, is the only son of God.

6. We believe that Jesus Christ was not formed by God but begotten by God.

7. We believe that Jesus Christ is God just as the Father is God.

8. We believe that Jesus is made of the same substance of God and the same substance of man.

9. We believe that Jesus was both fully God and fully man simultaneously, possessing both a soul and a physical body.

10. We believe the two natures of Jesus were inseparably combined in the same person, not parted or divided, and neither nature was superior to the other.

11. We believe that all things made by the Father were made through the Christ.

12. We believe that Jesus was made incarnate in human flesh and became man.

13. We believe that Jesus was born to Mary, a Virgin.

14. We believe that Mary was the *Theotokos*, truly carrying God in her womb.

15. We believe that Jesus became man in order to bring us our salvation.

16. We believe that Jesus lived a life like us in all ways except that He did so without committing sin.

17. We believe that Jesus suffered and was crucified at the hands of Pontius Pilate.

18. We believe that Jesus died, was buried, and rose from the grave on the third day.

19. We believe that Jesus ascended into heaven and is seated at the right hand of the Father.

20. We believe that Jesus will return to judge the living and the dead and establish an everlasting kingdom.

21. We believe in the Holy Ghost who speaks through the prophets.

22. We believe that the Holy Ghost is the Lord and is rightly worshipped with the Father and the Son.

23. We believe in a holy, universal Church.

24. We believe in one baptism for remission of sins.

25. We believe in the resurrection of the body and in everlasting life.

I should admit that many will complain about this list of beliefs; if so, their issues are not with me, but with historic Christian thought. Some will say that this is not enough. They will say that this allows too many people into heaven: too many Biblical illiterates, too many Catholics, too many Arminians, or too many of whichever Christian theology they dislike. I disagree. While others may have theologies which are more or less tightly bound to Jesus than yours, as long as they are within the boundaries of the above, then they pass the required litmus test to be Christian. They may be "at-risk" theologies, rotating only in the valence shell of theology, easily ripped out and made heretical; but as long as they remain within the boundaries above, then they remain Christians nonetheless, saved by the grace of God.

Others will say that I am too restrictive, that in the above list I exclude too many who identify as Christians; people like Gnostics and Mormons and theologically liberal churchgoers who attend church every week and are good people but do not actually believe in the "nonsense" that Jesus really lived and died and rose from the grave, that the Holy Ghost actively speaks to us, that our bodies will be resurrected for eternal life, that Jesus will judge us all at the end of time, and that He was REALLY God in the flesh. Again, they are wrong. They are not worshipping Christianity in any sort of historical sense, but simply a man-made religion of secularism.

Particularly frightening today is that many Christian pastors who are within the boundaries listed above tend to fall into one of two opposite errors when teaching.

Some (like many evangelical megachurch pastors) teach only a few tiny bits of doctrine, ignoring everything else as unimportant. They end up having a church filled with people who believe in some vague and undefined "Jesus" who repeated a sinner's prayer at the altar, but who do not actually believe the things that one must believe to be a Christian. How can they believe in the truths of Scripture, when they are not preached (Rom 10:14-15)? A church which does not teach the twenty-five key theologies above is actually a very bad place to be, as it gives unbelievers and heretics a false sense of security that they are saved when, in fact, they are lost. We are told in Matthew 7:22 that many will go to the judgment seat of Christ believing they are on good terms with God, only to find that they were never Christians at all.

On the other hand, we have many preachers today who slice doctrine so thinly and specifically that almost anyone who disagrees on any point is not a Christian: they try to take their particular interpretation and inflate it to being "the only possible truth." Thus God is blasphemously reduced to being a set of doctrines which a human can logically and completely define (despite the fact that Scripture repeatedly states that we are incapable of understanding all of God's mystery, for example, Job 38-40, Ps 77;14-19, Isa 55:8-9).

So I know that some will find the list too restrictive, others too inclusive. To both groups, I say again: your problem is not with me, but with historical Christianity. This is what being a Christian is about. This list is from the leaders of the first 25% of Christian history, those who were closest to the purity of apostolic teaching, and who lived before the Dark Ages set theology back significantly. They are the authors of the above twenty-five points, not me. It is exclusive to some belief systems, by its very nature; it is also inclusive to different theologies, different "shells" of atomic Christianity, as long as we are all orbiting the same Christ and Scripture described in the above twenty-five points. Based on this, I say that there will be a lot more people in heaven than some Christians think, a lot fewer people in heaven than most Christians think, and plenty of surprises to go around for us all. The best way to be certain you are there is to be sound on the twenty-five points above, and because of them let God do the work of justification and sanctification in you that He has desired.

– FIFTEEN –

SPIRITUAL RELATIVITY

As cool as classical physics is, modern physics is the scientific field which has the wonderful weirdness which attracts geeks the most, and which science fiction exploits in order to weave its fascinating tales. The two major branches of modern physics are quantum mechanics and relativity. We have discussed quantum mechanics quite a bit, so now let us spend some time discussing Einstein's theory of relativity.

Relativity has always fascinated me, and it also lends my wife endless amusement at my expense. In 1999, a film called *Deep Blue Sea* was released. In this absurd sci-fi movie, which I despise, sharks receive genetically superior brains. The sharks begin attacking everyone (because of course, making them smart means that they can instantly deduce how security cameras and electronics and pressurized submerged habitats work). The only good thing about the movie is that they mercifully kill off Samuel L. Jackson early, so that he could go work on good movies.

At one point while running from the sharks, LL Cool J says to the person next to him, "Einstein's theory of relativity. Grab hold of a hot pan, a second can seem like an hour; put your hands on a hot woman, an hour can seem like a second. It's all relative." The other character responds, "I spent four years at CalTech, and that's the best physics explanation I've ever heard."

Clearly the screenwriter did not spend four years at CalTech (or CalTech's physics department is not as good as I expected). LL here says that time is constant and our perception of it is relative to the situation; this is literally the exact opposite of Einstein's theory. So in case you learned your physics from the CalTech of the *Deep Blue Sea* universe, let's spend a bit of time understanding what Einstein's relativity actually says. (Note: Einstein's "relativity" actually consists of two separate theories, both of which are quite interesting: the Special Theory of Relativity and the General Theory of Relativity. I will discuss only the Special Theory of Relativity below, because it is the one which relates to my theological discussion.)

When Albert Einstein was 26, he studied the physics of motion, the result of which would be the Special Theory of Relativity. He began his investigation by starting with two foundational principles which must be understood in order to comprehend his results properly.

First Principle: Absolute motion cannot be detected.

The first principle Einstein assumed as a truth is simply an extension of what is sometimes called Newtonian relativity, because it has been well known by physicists as long ago as Newton and Galileo. This principle is best demonstrated through an example.

When my family was in China, we took a bullet train from Tianjin to Beijing. It was incredibly smooth, and topped out at just around 300 km/h in speed. Let's assume you boarded the bullet train, put on headphones and an eye mask, and promptly fell asleep. An unknown period of time later, you awoke. Is there any experiment you can do, without referring to something off of the train, which will tell you whether you are moving at a constant 300 km/h or standing still? Take some time and consider, but the answer is no. Without referring to some outside frame of reference (such as looking out the window, or feeling friction from the tracks), there is no way to tell whether you are standing still or moving at a smooth speed.

Now let's say you do look outside, and you see a train next to you. It appears to be slowly falling behind you. Is there any experiment you can do which can tell you whether you are moving? No. Maybe your train is perfectly still and they are moving backward; or maybe both of you are moving (but your train is a bit faster); or maybe they are at rest and you are just starting to slowly move.

As we begin to let this sink in and run more and more experiments, you will more clearly see the impact. Imagine that you are driving in Car A down the road. Next to you is Car B, which is falling behind you. You use a speed gun and determine that it is falling behind you at a rate of -20 km/h. So are you sitting still and it moving 20 km/h in reverse? Or are you traveling 20 km/h faster than it? Or is it at 0 and you are traveling 20 km/h? There is no way to tell just based upon your two reference frames; if they do the same experiment to you, they will simply see you moving forward at 20 km/h and also cannot tell the situation absolutely.

But now let us say that you both pass a police officer standing on the side of the road. Using his speed gun, he shows that Car A (yours) is traveling 100 km/h and Car B (your friend's) is traveling 80 km/h. So surely now, by using this new reference frame, we have the "true" record of motion, right? Wrong. All we have shown is that you are moving *past his frame of reference (the Earth)* at 100 km/h; that is, you are moving 100 km/h only relative to his point of view. An observer watching all of this from the moon would say that the policeman was traveling at 1,670 km/h, and you at 1770 km/h, and Car B at 1750 km/h – because relative to *his* frame of reference, you are all spinning quickly around the Earth's circumference. (Also you get a ticket. It was a 80 km/h zone; 1770 km/h is really pushing it.)

So you see all measurements of motion are completely dependent upon our frame of reference. There is no such thing as saying, "I am objectively moving at speed X," because there is no "objective" frame of reference for the physical world. All you can actually say is, "I am moving at 100 km/h compared to the policeman's frame of reference," or "I am moving at 20 km/h compared to my buddy's car," or "I am moving at 1,770 km/h compared to the moon astronaut." Every single frame of reference will measure your speed differently: the bird flying at you sees you traveling at one speed, while the astronaut sees you going another speed, while your dog sleeping in the backseat thinks he is sitting still, while the car next to you thinks you are driving like a maniac, while the trucker catching up to you from behind sees you as moving in reverse (coming toward him).

Ergo, all measurements of motion are relative to our frame of reference. No matter how hard you try, you cannot find an "objective" frame of reference; for there is none in the entire physical universe. Absolute motion cannot be detected by any means. Only relative motion (that is, "motion relative to some point that I arbitrarily chose") can be measured.

Second Principle: The speed of light always measures as the exact same value, c.

This was no more controversial at Einstein's time than the first principle. Any wave moves at the same speed regardless of the motion of the source, as has been demonstrated countless times. The speed that sound leaves my mouth and hits your ears does not change whether I am standing still or backing away from you; the distance between us may change (and thus it takes longer for the sound to reach you), but if you measure the speed of the sound it always comes up exactly the same. (Of course, the medium sound passes through may speed it up or slow it down; sound moves at different rates through air than water, for example. But the speed does not change even the tiniest bit depending upon motion.)

The same is true of light. No matter how sophisticated our measurements get, we see that it does not matter how fast a light source is traveling, light always moves at the rate of c (i.e., 299,792,458 m/s in a vacuum).

Einstein's genius

As mentioned, both of these principles had long been known to science and were by no means controversial. Einstein was no genius for noticing them. His genius came in realizing the inherent weirdness associated with this truth.

Let us return to our car analogy. If I am driving Car A and I turn on a flashlight, we would think (based on the First Principle) that light should act just like anything else: that is, its speed should be relative. In Car A, I should measure the light as leaving at a speed of c. Car B should measure it as moving at $c+20$ km/h. The policeman should measure it as $c+100$ km/h. The person on the moon should measure it as $c+1770$ km/h. We are all in different frames of reference, so we should all get different speeds, right?

But that isn't what happens. Not at all. All of these observers see the light as traveling at the same speed.

The results of Einstein's observation are very intriguing. Most surprisingly, we find that these observations *require* that time is not constant. We of course perceive it as passing at a constant rate, due to the effects of entropy and our limited perceptive abilities; we also cannot "perceive" that we are currently spinning at 1770 km/h around Earth's core, but that does not make it untrue. Einstein showed that in order for light to travel the same speed in all frames of reference, time must actually pass slower on the faster-moving reference frames. Thus the faster you go, the slower time passes for you! So if your twin travels away from you at near-light speed for several years and returns, he only has aged 8 years while you aged 20 years! This effect is called *time dilation.*

As strange as this might seem, we can directly test this and it has proved accurate thousands of times. Scientists have synchronized two atomic clocks and then put one on an airplane at high speed, while leaving the other on the ground. When they were brought back together, the faster-moving clock showed fewer "ticks" had passed than the slower-moving clock. The faster speed at which it moved actually slowed time. Literally speaking, when you fly to a vacation you age more slowly than if you drive there!

One great example deals with the production of muons (a tiny, negatively charged particle). Muons appear in the atmosphere as a secondary radiation from cosmic rays. Muons only live about 2 microseconds (or two millionths of a second) before degrading. A typical muon hitting the atmosphere would be moving at $0.9978c$, and therefore should fall only about 600 m before its two microsecond life ends. Thus very few would be expected to hit the ground; statistically, only 3 per 10,000,000 would actually land on the ground. However, this is not what relativity predicts. Because they are moving so quickly, relativity would predict that time would pass very slowly from the muon's point of view. Thus two microseconds of life for the muon would feel like much longer to us, as it is moving so much faster than us. Relativity would predict that time passed so slowly on the muon that instead of 3 per 10,000,000 muons hitting the Earth we should see 3.7 *million* muons survive to hit the Earth! Sure enough, when the experiment is performed, this is what we see. Repeated experiments like this have shown that relativity absolutely is correct: time passes slower on fast-moving objects than slow-moving ones. We can be as certain of this as we are that a thrown ball will fall to the Earth due to gravity. (To see the calculations, see Tipler, 3rd Ed., p. 1251-1252).

What does this mean? Well, it means that our perception of events is relative to our frames of reference and therefore not absolute. Yet it also means that there is one objective yardstick (the speed of light) which is always the same, regardless of your perception. As a result, this dilates time itself, so that the passage of time we perceive on an object is not absolute, but varies based upon our frame of reference.

+ + + theology: judgmentalism + + +

As we saw in chapter ten, and shall see again in the following chapters, we will one day all stand before the Great White Throne of Christ in judgment. There will our souls, beliefs, and actions be judged and seen for what they are. What is sad, however, is how many Christians appear to think that their job in the Kingdom of God is to start White-Throne-Judging those around them today. Nothing could be further from the truth.

In Matthew 5-7, during the famous Sermon on the Mount, Jesus talks about the moral law and makes it clear that none of us measure up. He tells us that we must be perfect as God is perfect (5:48). He tells us that we cannot get angry, lust, divorce, make oaths, fight back against attackers, hold grudges against enemies, keep our money for ourselves while others are in need, gain approval from others for our piety, horde wealth, or worry...it is a pretty overwhelming list. That was His purpose.

This is the yardstick by which God judges. These are the specifications which we earlier discussed. But what is intriguing is that Jesus talks about one subject almost as much as any other in His teachings: judgmentalism. He is absolutely passionate, at times seemingly obsessed, with ensuring that we leave the judging of other people's sins up to Him and Him alone.

He is actually very, very specific on this issue. In Matt 6:12, He tells us to ask God to forgive us of our sins in direct proportion to how well we have forgiven the sins of others. In Matt 6:14-15, He explicitly says that if we do not forgive others of their sins against us, God will not forgive us of our sins. In Matt 7:1-5, He says that we are not to judge others or we will be judged by God. In Matt 5:44, He says that when dealing with our enemies we must forgive them and love them, and let God worry about justice. In John 8:7, He says that we cannot judge even obvious sins unless we are ourselves sinless.

We see this elsewhere in Scripture also. In Romans 14:4, Paul says that only the master has the right to judge a servant, so we have no right to judge another believer. In 1 Cor 4:3-5 Paul says that others should not judge him, but if they do he does not care, for he does not judge even himself. In James 4:11-12, Jesus' brother says that judging someone else's moral failures is akin to claiming to be God.

Now, often Jesus says that He has the right to judge others (Luke 12:49-51; John 9:39; John 3:19), and we are told that we are to judge *the things people teach* to determine if they are truly teaching the Gospel or not (1 John 4:1-3, Matt 7:15-20, 1 Tim 6:3-5). But we are forbidden to judge whether someone else is saved, or "right with the Lord," or living sinfully. Jesus says that we are to teach the Scripture truly, and love each other radically, and pray for each other constantly...and let God handle the judging. The early Christians took this so seriously that Tertullian recommended avoiding being a boss or serving in politics, lest your actions accidentally be taken as judging someone else's life!

Why is this? Why doesn't Jesus let us be His judges here on Earth, and tell those around us how they should be living and determining whether they are real believers or not? The reason is something that I call Spiritual Relativity.

Let me begin with two principles, just as Einstein did:

First Principle: Absolute state of the heart cannot be detected.

Just as we cannot determine absolute motion due to our reference frames, so too is it impossible for us to judge others rightly because we cannot truly understand them. We cannot know what is in their hearts and minds when they commit their sins. We cannot know whether, or how much, they love God. We cannot know what hardships they face. We cannot know their situations. We are hopelessly subjective: we see only what their outside actions are for a brief window of time and, therefore, draw conclusions about the state of their souls. I am guilty of this as well: I have known co-workers who outside of work are outspoken Christian leaders, and at work are foul-mouthed and untrustworthy; it is quite hard not to judge them. But I only see them for perhaps a few hours each week, and if I judge them, I do so with no understanding of their history, context, home life, work life, calling from Christ, or what the Holy Spirit is convicting them of at this moment in their Christian growth. It is completely wrong for me to judge, because I do not know *them*, only a small amount of data gathered from my subjective frame of reference.

I am hopelessly subjective. I cannot know some things (such as what is going on in their hearts and minds or in the 99% of their lives that I do not personally witness); I choose not to know other things (instead, snapping to judgment rather than giving the benefit of the doubt); and I have never experienced whatever hardships they experience (but instead have had a quite comfortable life).

Just as it was with measuring motion, there is no objective reference available for us sinful humans to use to fairly judge each other. We cannot ever know enough to make a fair judgment of another person. The minute we judge others, we inherently become hypocrites, for the very things that we judge others for, we do.

"No," you may say. "That is not true. I am no murderer. I am no adulterer." Jesus says you are.

In Matt 5:21-26, Jesus says that if you have ever been angry at someone, you are guilty of murdering him in your heart and owe a debt to Hell. In Matt 5:27-30, Jesus says that lusting over a woman is the same as committing adultery with her. This principle abounds throughout Scripture; sins of the heart are equal to sins of the flesh.

Why would that be? Because of your reference frame. Say that you and your co-worker go on a business trip. You are both at a bar drinking and lusting about a local woman. You go up to your room and lust for her all night, but fall asleep alone and do not act outwardly on your lust. Your marriage is intact and your sin is hidden to everyone but God. Your co-worker sleeps with the woman, gets her pregnant, and now has an illegitimate child and a mess to discuss at home.

Jesus says you are both equally guilty and deserving of hell.

Why? Because you both had the same actual sin (lust). Something about your reference frame (your upbringing, your happy relationship to your wife, a fear of getting caught, a fear of STDs, better education, a calmer personality, etc.) kept you from committing adultery. But your friend, in a different reference frame, committed adultery. His sin has more earthly consequences than yours, and can ruin his life on Earth worse than your sin; but both are still equally sins.

For you to judge him is flat-out wrong; you, in his position and with his background, might in fact have made exactly the same mistake.

How radically will I take this grace? How far will I stretch it? How about this: do not judge the Germans who allowed the Nazis to do horrible things to the Jews. It is very easy for you to judge them from the comfort of your wealthy American living room. But in the midst of war, with the Nazi government executing Germans who opposed them, how can you be certain you would not have committed the same sin? A lot of Americans judged the Nazis for racial concentration camps and then turned around and started doing the same thing (minus the executions) to Japanese-Americans living here a few short years later.

The point is, do not judge others because you cannot know their hearts, their backgrounds, or their situations. You do not know what you would do in their situation. Love them and pity them; say, "There but for the grace of God go I." But do not judge them. It is not your right; you do not have the objective viewpoint necessary to hold others accountable for their sins. Jesus is so serious about this, that He says if you judge others then He is going to judge you the same way; and since you don't know what their insides look like, you had better be very careful about comparing yourself to them, lest you be found to be even worse!

Our sinful, spiritual gravity loves to make us compare ourselves to others. In our minds, all of our successes are because of our willpower, but our failures are because of Adam and Eve's sin or someone else for tempting us. Nothing is *really* our fault. But everyone else's sin? That is all on them, isn't it? You lack their frame of reference, and thus you fail to give them the same grace you so liberally apply to your own life.

The fact is that none of us can objectively judge. Take an illiterate man, raised in the projects with a fourth grade education, born to a mother on cocaine and raised around drugs, alcohol, and gangs. Now compare to me, with my educated middle-class upbringing, wonderful family life, and all of the advantages of education and money. *It is entirely possible that me yelling at my son is a BIGGER sin than the hypothetical man mugging someone.* It is possible that him pistol-whipping someone instead of shooting them might be a bigger act of kindness than me giving 10% of my salary to the church. It is all a matter of reference frame, and none of us can objectively and absolutely judge the truth of a matter except Jesus.

Second Principle: Christ's death is sufficient to cover all sin, regardless of the frame of reference.

When we talked about physical relativity, it seemed natural to us that the speed of light would be added to our velocity, just as with throwing a ball from our car. But it turned out that regardless of your frame of reference, light travels at the same speed.

In spiritual relativity, a similar effect occurs. For the born-again believer, for he who has Christ's grace filling his heart, Christ's death is seen as sufficient for all of his sins (past/present/future), regardless of how bad they are. So whether the believer is an illiterate thug who has killed twenty people, a serial rapist, or a middle-aged engineer with an excessive concern about what others think of him, Christ's death on the cross is sufficient for all—it is not too much for some and too little for others, but equally sufficient.

Just as we do not have to add to the speed of light to account for existing velocity, or subtract from the speed of light if it is shot at a receding object, neither do we have to add to or subtract from Christ's death in order to justify us for our sins. His death is sufficient for all that we have done or will ever do, if we love God. Thus we can be confident in the sufficiency of the Cross.

Belote's Theory of Spiritual Relativity

So let us follow the same logic in our spiritual discussion that Einstein used for the physical realm. Einstein noted that the frame of reference did not change our measurements, and that the speed of light remained a consistent yardstick in all frames of reference. Thus he saw that there was another measurement, time, which must be dilated (contracted in some cases, expanded in others) to satisfy the mathematics.

In the same way, you can think of our sin as undergoing *sin dilation*. It is of course true that I have sinned less than, say, a serial child molester. But if we both turn to Christ, the same death is required for us both, even though our sins are different. Why is that? Why would I not just require a partial punishment of Christ (say, a crown of thorns) while a mass murderer might require years of torture?

The reason, I say, is sin dilation. (Of course I do not say that this is a real, true, *thing*; rather, consider it simply an analogy). I have had an easy life. There is no way around it: I live in a great state in a great country. My parents raised me well, invested in my education, and encouraged me to succeed. I have had people both at work and in church invest in me and make me better. I have a wife who is amazing and two kids who make parenting easy. I have an incredible support system, from amazing in-laws to great extended family like aunts and uncles and cousins and grandparents who are always there for me. On top of it all, I have the Holy Spirit guiding and loving me and saving me in spite of myself. Considering my upbringing, I should easily be able to have the self-control to live a holy lifestyle and not make the stupid mistakes I make.

A factory worker I know, though, was raised in a home so poor that once I took him to Red Lobster after work and had to help him order off of a menu; even at age 19 he had never been at a sit down restaurant. (The nicest place he had been was the Pizza Hut buffet.) He had a child out of wedlock as a teenager. He is a poor kid who, though nice when you get to know him, is shy (due to his poor education) and huge, so he comes across as a thug and intimidating. He grew up in the kind of family where it was considered normal for him to get drunk (though underage) at a family event and drive his son home afterward. When he got in a car wreck, his infant was killed. Considering his upbringing, it seems a miracle that things are not worse and that the vehicular manslaughter and DUI are his only brushes with the law; after all, everyone else he grew up with is in a gang and on welfare while dealing drugs.

But if we are both Christians, then our sins equally require Christ's death. His death neither has to expand to cover my friend's sins, nor contract to cover mine. His death was fully needed for my sins, and still sufficient for my friend's sins.

This implies that our sins themselves are dilated, just as time is dilated when you move quickly. If you had a really easy path, even your minor sins seem major; if you had a terrible life, then even minor kindnesses you show might be considered great virtue. The sin dilates such that they are judged fairly *relative to the situation in which the sinner was placed.* So my sin of omission when I drive past a poor homeless man instead of giving him money may end up being worse than the years of theft he has done to steal food for dinner. It is sin dilation: the sin is judged relative to the genetic and environmental situation we are in, which explains why we are all equally in need of the same death of Christ.

And this is precisely why we must avoid judgmentalism. In the wrong frame of reference we may have ended up being Nazis or warlords or drug addicts. Do not underestimate the extent to which your frame of reference protected you from further sin; you have no concept of just how bad your sins have been, given the blessings you have been provided. How bad is it? So bad that even though you feel like a pretty good person, both you and a mass murderer are *equally in need of Christ's death.* The different reference frames merely result in a dilation of your sin; it does not lessen your need for atonement.

And if you need Christ's death as much as the next guy, then you have no moral high ground from which to judge. Only Christ can judge, for the Biblical word *krino* ("judge") directly implies a magistrate sitting on a judgment seat, with the authority and right to pronounce legal judgment against the prisoner on trial. If you judge another believer for his sin, then you will be judged the same way for yours. As Jesus said in Mark 4:24, "with the measure you use, it will be measured to you"; and again, in John 8:7, "Let he who is without sin cast the first stone." Were the Jews in John 8 wrong that the woman was an adulterer? Not at all! But Jesus said that they had no right to judge her: the right was His, not theirs. In fact, of the 114 uses of *krino* in the New Testament, 85% show either God or a legally-authorized magistrate as judge, or are explicit prohibitions against Christian judgmentalism. The right to judge is held by the Holy Spirit (Jo 16:11), and to take that from Him is a kind of usurpation and blasphemy. Indeed, the only authority for judging which is delegated to Christians is the commandment that we judge false teaching, the requirement that some will serve as judges in Heaven, and the duty of church leadership for excommunication (Matt 18:15-20, 19:28; Luk 22:30; Jo 7:24).

It must be noted, however, that some Christians understand the above and yet swing the pendulum too far in the other direction. They follow an approach more like the Stoics of Greece than the Christians, believing that *offending* someone is the same as *judging* them. Of course people will sometimes be offended by learning about sin, and seeing themselves as sinners. Lack of judgmentalism does not mean hiding what Scripture says about sin. Rather, we should follow the guidance of the apostles in the book of Acts, who managed to share a great deal about sin and yet never be accused of judgmentalism. They did this by building relationships with people first, and sharing the Gospel honestly and openly when approached. In fact, this was by far the dominant mode of apostolic evangelism: build a relationship, show people what a Christian life looks like through sacrificial love, and be prepared to share your beliefs when they are interested in having spiritual discussions. Of the more than thirty examples of the Gospel being shared in the book of Acts, 97% of the time the discussion was raised *by the unbeliever*—either because the apostles had done some good work for them, or because the apostles had reputations as wise philosophers and were invited to speak in public. This focus—to build relationships as a means of sharing the Gospel—requires a lack of judgmentalism of others, for no one wishes to build relationships with someone who is condemning them.

Let this then become the rule in your life: remember in humility that Christ's death was fully needed for your own sin, and that He Himself is responsible for judging others of their sin. He does not need your help in that regard. Let Him do His job. If you understand this spiritual relativity, then you will be able to share God's Gospel plainly and clearly, and talk about sin not as a judge but as a fellow prisoner whose shackles have been broken.

– SIXTEEN –

R2-D2, SPY EXTRAORDINAIRE

Muslims versus Jews. Catholics versus Protestants. North versus South. China versus Japan. America versus Russia. Germany versus Everyone. There have been a lot of heated rivals throughout history, but one rivalry beats them all:

Star Wars versus *Star Trek.*

This is the Civil War of geekdom. Both side have their strengths, of course. Star Trek (and its many spin-offs) is one of the most successful science fiction franchises of all time. Kirk, Spock, Scotty, Bones, Pickard, Warf, Data, Whoopi...many of the characters have become iconic and influenced a great deal of pop culture. In all honesty I should be a Star Trek guy. Star Trek is pure science fiction, set in the future of our part of the universe, where we are using our technological advancements to explore the galaxies. Star Wars is much more like fantasy lit than science fiction; it is more Tolkien or Lewis than Clarke or Asimov. In Star Wars, the plot advances not due to cool technology, but due to a mystical control of the "force." Star Trek is the true science fiction story.

And yet, I am decidedly a Star Wars guy. Growing up, it was the Millennium Falcon, not the Enterprise, which I pictured myself piloting. R2 was my helpful droid, not Data. I am still enthralled with the iconic scene of the AT-ATs walking across the bright white snow in *Empire Strikes Back*, and love seeing Luke appear in *Return of the Jedi* in his full power.

But both Star Wars and Star Trek deal have a similar problem: story conflicts. Both were written by a variety of writers long before they realized how much geeks would analyze every tiny aspect of their work. So there are logical inconsistencies, contradictions in the storyline, for both stories. These are called *continuity errors*, and for long-running shows like Star Trek and Doctor Who, or shows with many spin-offs like Star Wars, or comic book universes, maintaining a world with consistent continuity so that all stories make sense together is very difficult.

Often, therefore, writers use a process called *retcon*, short for "retroactive continuity": it is the creation of some plot device which undoes past work, thus returning the universe to a state of continuity. Doctor Who introduced concepts of a Time War and "cracks in the universe" to help explain away past discontinuities. 2009's new *Star Trek* movie used time travel as a retcon device to explain variances across its past versions.

Retcons become necessary when two stories from the accepted *canon* of a series contradict one another or are not easily explainable on the surface level. By using the word canon, geeks are consciously using religious terminology: just as a Protestant's canon includes both the Old and New Testament, but excludes other books written from the period, so too does a geek show have a "canon" and a "non-canon." The *canon* of a series is the official, accepted storyline of a fictional universe, and the *non-canon* are works written about this universe but which can be ignored if they contradict. Contradictions within the canon are considered a major blow to the fun of a series, while non-canon is considered "unofficial" and thus problems can be ignored. So if the *Star Wars: The Clone Wars* cartoons disagree with the movies, it is okay: the cartoons are not canon anyway. No explanation is needed.

Star Wars canon did not really have any major problems...in the original three movies. They were nearly perfect. And then George Lucas had to go and punish all of his loyal fans by making the prequels. Episodes I, II, and III were, it is safe to say, objectively awful. The dialog was awful. The acting was awful. The plotlines were awful. Jar-Jar Binks was...do I even need to say how bad Jar-Jar was, or has the universal hatred of all fellow fanboys sufficed?

Worst of all, the prequels added into Star Wars some really large contradictions. In *A New Hope* (episode four, the original Star Wars film), Jedi Obi-Wan Kenobi said that he did not know the droids R2D2 and C3PO. Yet in the prequels we see that they actually flew around together for years. We find out that Chewbacca—who in the original trilogy was just a smuggler's first mate and seemed to only get involved in the rebellion by accident—was actually involved in the Clone Wars and knew Yoda personally. In the original trilogy, the Millennium Falcon ship is a fast clunker used by no-name smuggler Han Solo, having been won from another shady character (Lando) in a gambling game. But in the prequels we see that Millennium Falcon was used by allies of the Jedi in the Battle of Coruscant, indicating that it had been closely connected to the story the entire time. Lucas appears to have tried to retcon some of the problems by erasing C3PO's memory in Episode III, but forgot to do the same to R2D2. This leaves many open plot holes, not least of which is how unlikely it is that Obi-Wan just so happens to end up as a hermit down the road from where Anakin's unknown son lives.

In 2005, a Star Wars geek named Keith Martin (whom I do not know) posted a lengthy retcon on the Internet, attempting to explain away all the Star Wars inconsistencies in one fell swoop. Martin's argument centers around a single assumption: R2D2 and Chewbacca are actually rebel spies, and probably the most important characters of the entire series.

Martin's retcon accepts the prequels as canon. Chewbacca is the second in command of Kashykk, his home planet, and its best general. He and Yoda work together during battles. Later, when we see the Millennium Falcon land on the Senate building, Martin supposes that (rather than just an absurd coincidence) it is actually a diplomatic mission from Kashykk, because the Millennium Falcon is actually Chewbacca's ship. When the Sith win at the end of *Revenge of the Sith*, the rebellion is formed; its key leaders are Bail Organa, Obi-Wan, and Yoda. Yoda and Obi-Wan are too high profile targets as Jedi, so they go into hiding (Yoda to the swamps of Dagobah, and Obi-Wan to Tatooine, the home planet of Anakin Skywalker). Anakin, now Darth Vader, became the father of twins before his wife died, but he was unaware that they survived. Bail Organa adopts the daughter (Leia) as his own, while sending Luke back to his uncle's farm on Tatooine. Obi-Wan keeps an eye on Luke from a distance—if he shows signs of becoming another Vader, Obi-Wan will kill him.

Organa, to protect the new Rebel Alliance, wipes the memory of C3PO. But R2D2—an expert hacker who has proved himself useful to the Jedi many times—is spared and recruited into the rebellion. Chewbacca is also recruited. Chewbacca manages to "lose" his ship to Lando in a gambling debt, thus allowing him to sneak throughout the Empire, recruiting and delivering messages, under the guise of being a smuggler. Meanwhile R2D2 and C3PO seem to just be regular droids when in fact R2 is constantly hacking into government systems and stealing information. This is how he gets the plans at the beginning of *A New Hope*; he did not receive them from Leia, but already had them. All Leia does is record the message for Obi-Wan.

When Obi-Wan sees the droids in *A New Hope*, he calls R2 "My little friend" before saying that he had never owned droids before. This was his way of letting R2 know that Luke was still in the dark about the rebels and R2 needed to keep quiet.

This explanation really does clear up a lot of plot holes, and actually makes the original trilogy a lot more fun to watch. Some of R2's chirps and squeaks seem to have a lot more meaning behind them, and his battles with aging Yoda in the swamps and over chess with Chewbacca have a much more "comrade-in-arms" brotherhood feel to them.

What Martin did with this explanation is a perfect example of retconning: he provided an explanation which fits within the *canonical* description but which helps resolve supposed controversies, bringing a great deal of clarity to the story.

For a retcon to work convincingly, it must be able to look freshly at the canon statement of facts, and be willing to ignore the traditional interpretations of those facts. If one tries to accept the canon of the six Star Wars films using only the interpretations of the casual fan, then they cannot explain all of the contradictions. But because Martin was able to clearly separate the *facts* from the *interpretations* in the Star Wars universe, he was able to provide a very convincing description which actually added a great deal of value to the discussion.

+ + + theology: Hell and the Afterlife + + +

If you are wondering why I chose Star Wars as the introductory story to a chapter about Hell, then you clearly have not seen the Hell-on-Earth that Lucas created in his prequels and (even worse) the "improved" original trilogy. (I don't know what is worse: changing it so that Han did not shoot first in the

Cantina scene, or the painfully awkward scene of Han and Jabba walking and talking together.)

In actuality, the reason that I chose it is because the concept of separating canon fact from common interpretation is also necessary in order to approach what the Bible actually says about the afterlife.

Due to movies, television, stories, and just common culture, most Christians—long before they actually can read the Bible for themselves—have a preconceived notion of what the afterlife is like. They see the afterlife as working like this: when you die, you are judged and go to Heaven or Hell. Heaven is a bunch of people in white sheets floating on clouds playing harps. Hell is a bunch of caves with fire and brimstone and demons everywhere, and the devil is there punishing everyone with his pitchfork and tail and horns.

Because they have this interpretation, they bring this context into their reading of the Bible, which greatly influences how they understand the Scriptures. This has, sadly, greatly affected even some otherwise excellent theologians, leading occasionally to misinterpretations and alleged contradictions.

What I propose is a retcon: let us see what our canon (the Old and New Testaments) actually *factually* says about the afterlife, and from this we can discuss a number of different potential interpretations.

The Canon/Facts

One of the confusions Christians have about the afterlife comes from the notion already in our minds ("Clouds = Heaven and Fiery Caves = Hell"). Because this is the context we bring to the reading, we tend to ignore the fact that the Bible actually uses a lot of different words (not just two) to discuss the afterlife. We just translate these all as either "Heaven" or "Hell," and thus we lose the context of what the Bible is actually saying. The chance of reading only the facts is lost. So let us begin by listing and discussing all of the different terms used in the Bible to discuss the afterlife.

At this point we will only discuss the facts; we will discuss potential retcons/interpretations later.

Sheol/Hades

As we discussed in chapter five, at the moment of our death, our souls are separated from our physical bodies. While our physical bodies rot in the ground and "return to dust" (Gen 3:19), the soul lives on in an intermediate place usually translated as the "grave." In Hebrew, the word for this place is *sheol* (e.g.: Gen 37:35; Gen 44:31; Deut 32:22; 1 Sam 2:6; 2 Sam 22:6; Job 7:9; many others).

This term *sheol* is used in several different contexts; sometimes it is seen as a place for unrighteous, sometimes it is used to refer to all of the dead. It certainly would appear from the Old Testament uses that *sheol* is a place where the souls of all of the dead end up, and at least part of *sheol* is reserved for the unrighteous, who will be punished.

This is further bolstered by the fact that when the Jewish rabbis translated the Hebrew Old Testament into Greek (the *Septuagint* version of the Old Testament), they chose the word *hades* to represent *sheol*. In Greek mythology, *hades* was the land of dead souls and had different sections within it (the great pit of Tartarus for the damned, and the Elysian Fields for the righteous). The Jewish rabbis apparently believed that the word *hades* carried enough similarity to the Biblical description of *sheol* that the two could be used as synonyms of one another.

For example, let us take Isaiah 38:18, which we translate as: "For Sheol does not thank you; death does not praise you; those who go down into the pit do not hope for your faithfulness." The "pit" here is seen as a separate location from *sheol*, implying that there is a part of *sheol* reserved for suffering. When translated into the Greek, the rabbis felt that *hades* was an appropriate translation for *sheol*; this makes sense, as the Greek concept of *hades* also had a pit for the damned, Tartarus. (Of course, the Greek myth ends with *hades*, for the material world to them was impure; Christians are very different, believing that we will be reunited with our bodies and that *hades* is only a pit stop on our way to eternal life, not the end of the road.)

In the New Testament era, most of the people used Greek as their common trade language and read the Old Testament in its Septuagint translation. Indeed, many of the apostles in the New Testament, when quoting the Old Testament, quote from the Septuagint. So it is probably not surprising that the New Testament continues the use of the word *hades* when referring to the grave (e.g., Acts 2:27, Matt 16:18, Luke 16:22).

Many commentators simply equate *hades* with Hell, the location of eternal punishment, but this is an interpretation, not a Scriptural fact. As we shall see, there is a completely different word used for this, so we must be careful not to simply assume the two are equivalent. In fact, Rev 20:12-13 indicates that the two are separate places: on Judgment Day, all of the dead are taken from *hades* and judged, and those who are unrighteous go not back to *hades*, but to the Lake of Fire (more on this later).

Another point of interest with regard to *hades* is that, in Acts 2:31, we see that Jesus went to *hades* after His death; later Peter tells us that He spent those three days preaching to the lost souls (1 Pet 3:18-19).

Thus we may take it as canonical that *sheol* and *hades* both refer to the same place: it is an intermediate location where the souls of the dead, separated from the body, exist while waiting for Judgment Day. These dead souls are separated based upon their righteousness.

Abraham's Side

In Luke 16:19-31, Jesus tells a parable about a rich man and a beggar named Lazarus, both of whom died. When they died, Lazarus was taken to "Abraham's side" (or Abraham's "bosom," in some translations), while the rich man was taken to *hades* and was in agony. The two are said to be separated by a great chasm so that no one could cross to the other side, yet both souls could see and speak to one another (v.26).

Generally speaking, most theologians interpret Abraham's Side as either "in Heaven with God," or as the "righteous" part of *hades*. Both of these are interpretations, though. All that we can say strictly from the canon is that Abraham's Side is a place separate from the part of *hades* where souls are punished, it exists prior to the resurrection of the dead bodies, and it is somehow associated with Abraham (who was the father of the Jewish people as well as the example of ideal faith).

Gehenna / The Lake of Fire

Gehenna is a word used to refer to the Valley of the Son of Hinnom, a valley outside of Jerusalem (Josh 15:8, 18:16). King Ahaz of Judah defiled this valley when he sacrificed his illegitimate children by burning them alive to the pagan gods (2 Chr 28:3). Isaiah referred to it simply as "the burning place" and the place where the "worm does not die" (Isa 30:33, 66:24). It appears that a shrine to the pagan god Moloch was built here, and child sacrifice was not uncommon (2 Chr 28:3; 33:6; Jer 7:31).

In its Old Testament usage, Gehenna simply refers to this physical valley of fire sacrifice to idols. In the New Testament, Jesus chooses this term (not *hades*) to refer to what we typically think of as Hell—the place of eternal punishment for those who are not allowed into the Kingdom of God. (His brother, in James 3:6, uses this word the same way.) Jesus describes it as a place where both body and soul are destroyed (Matt 10:28); as a place where the fires cannot be put out (Mark 9:43); and as a place where God casts the unrighteous (Luke 12:5). In other words, Gehenna is the word Jesus used to describe what we typically think of when we picture "Hell": a place of fire and eternal torment. Whenever Jesus speaks about eternal punishment after the resurrection of the body, He uses the term Gehenna, not *hades*.

He tells us that our anger – not only our murder – makes us liable to Gehenna (Matt 5:22); He tells us that it is better to cut off body parts that make us sin than for our whole body to be cast into Gehenna (Matt 5:29-30; 18:9; Mark 9:43-47). He tells us that the Pharisees will find it difficult to avoid being sentenced to Gehenna (Matt 23:33), and that when they convert someone to their way of thinking it is like damning the person to Gehenna all over again (Matt 23:15).

What is very interesting is that Jesus gives us a critical contextual clue. We can state with complete factual certainty that Gehenna is **not** a place where souls end up before the Final Judgment. When we die, our bodies are separated from our souls, and our souls will not be rejoined to our bodies until the resurrection of our bodies after Christ's Second Coming (Rev 20:13). Therefore when Jesus says that Gehenna is where bodies and souls are thrown, we know that going to Gehenna is something which happens after the Final Judgment.

The phrase *"lake of fire"* is used in Revelation, and refers to a place prepared for Satan and his angels. It is said to be "burning with fire and sulfur." It is a place where the beast and false prophet of Revelation are tormented eternally (Rev 19:20; 20:10; 21:8). And this is the place where the unrighteous are ultimately sent. So we clearly can conclude that the "lake of fire" and "Gehenna" refer to the same location – the concept we typically think of as Hell.

Tartarus

In 2 Peter 2:4, we are told that when the fallen angels sinned against God, He did something to them called *"tartaroo,"* which is commonly translated as "cast into hell." The verse in the ESV, for example, says, "...God did not spare angels when they sinned, but *cast them into hell* and committed them to chains of gloomy darkness *to be kept until the judgment.*"

Right away we know that, since they are being held there pending final judgment, this is not Gehenna, since no one is there until after the Judgment Day. Also recall that in Acts 2 and 1 Pet 3:18-19, Peter told us that Jesus went to *hades*, where He "preached to the spirits in prison."

This makes Peter's choice of the word *tartaroo* all the more interesting, because it literally means "throw to Tartarus." In Greek mythology, Tartarus was the pit inside of *hades* where the worst spirits (like the Titans) and other damned souls were held and punished according to their sins. By using this term, it seems that Peter is clearly equating Tartarus with the "unrighteous" part of *hades*, where Jesus spent three days preaching to the lost before He rose from the grave.

Therefore we may conclude with some certainty that Tartarus is the name give by Peter to the unrighteous section of *hades*.

Paradise

In Luke 23:43, Jesus says to one of the criminals being crucified alongside Him, "Truly, I say to you, today you will be with me in Paradise."

It is on the basis of this verse that many people see us going to the Kingdom of Heaven immediately when we die. However, we need to remember that this is an interpretation, not a fact. It may be true, or it may not. As we saw earlier (1 Pet 3:18-19, Acts 2:31), Jesus did not go to the Kingdom of Heaven when He died, but spent three days in *hades*, preaching to the spirits who were there awaiting judgment. So when He promises that He and the criminal will be "together *today in Paradise*," what does this mean, knowing that Jesus would go to *hades* on that day?

We will discuss possible interpretations of this later.

The Outer Darkness

In addition, three times Jesus refers to people being cast into the "outer darkness" (Matt 8:12; 22:13; 25:30). In Matthew 8, He says that many Gentiles will be feasting in heaven with Abraham, Isaac, and Jacob while Israelites are cast into the outer darkness. In Matthew 22, He again says that the Israelites who rejected Him will be cast into outer darkness and not be a part of the wedding feast (which in that usage, symbolizes resurrection into heaven); in Matthew 25, He says that those who claimed to be servants of God but hid what God gave them and did nothing with it will be cast into the outer darkness. In all three cases, He says that there will be weeping and gnashing of teeth, indicating that some will be sad (weeping) and others will be angry (gnashing of teeth).

Judgment Day

Very little actually exists in Scripture to clarify how the judgment of man happens. In Revelation, John has a vision of God on a great white throne.

Hades gives up its dead and these dead souls assemble before the throne for judgment (Rev 20:12-13). The books with their works are opened, sharing their deeds.

(Recall that as we saw in chapter three, the deeds of man are hopelessly sinful and selfish; yet in chapter ten we received a promise that, when believers are viewed by God, all He will see is the "Jesus" part of our dual nature, and our sinfulness will collapse and cease to exist.)

Those who are believers have their names "found in the Book of Life" (Rev 20:13), and thus survive to enter the Kingdom of God (next chapter). Those whose names are not found in the Book of Life are judged fairly by their works—and a fair judgment means that none are good enough to enter God's kingdom of perfection. Thus, they are cast into Gehenna, the lake of fire (Rev 20:14). This is called the Second Death.

Summary of Facts

So then, the canonical facts of the afterlife (which any interpretation must include in order to be Biblically acceptable) are these:

1. After death, the soul is separated from the body.

2. The souls of all people go to *hades* (or *sheol* in Hebrew) the good in one section and the unrighteous in another section.

3. Jesus spent three days in *hades* after He died, preaching to the spirits in prison.

4. Jesus tells a parable where a man is being punished in *hades* while a righteous man is in "Abraham's bosom," a location of joy separated from the area of punishment by an un-crossable chasm.

5. When Jesus talks about eternal judgment, He calls it Gehenna, referring to an evil shrine used in Israel's past to burn child sacrifices.

6. Jesus and James both say that sins result in eternal judgment in Gehenna.

7. Jesus says that the unrighteous will have bodies again before being cast into Gehenna.

8. John calls the place of eternal punishment in Revelation a "lake of fire."

9. On Judgment Day, the dead souls will be removed from *hades* and re-united to their bodies.

10. Those who are found unrighteous will be cast into the lake of fire.

11. Peter calls the part of *hades* where evil spirits are imprisoned "Tartarus," which in Greek terminology was a pit for the damned.

12. Jesus promises one of the criminals that they would be together in paradise that some day.

13. On occasion, Jesus refers to those left out of the Kingdom of God as being in the "outer darkness."

Any interpretation we have must explain all thirteen of these facts.

Interpretations

Of course, there are hundreds of ways to interpret these statements of fact, but some make more sense than others. The key thing to remember is that they are *interpretations*, not direct quotes from Scripture. Thus, they might be incorrect. All we can say with certainty about the afterlife is what is included within the above thirteen facts.

I am not going to list all of the possible interpretations, but let me give one good example of an interpretation which easily fits all of the facts:

When we die, our souls are separated from our bodies. Our souls go to *hades*, an intermediate holding-place where the souls await final judgment. One side of *hades* is Abraham's Side, also called Paradise; this is where the righteous souls await judgment. Across a chasm is a large area for the lost souls. In this unrighteous part of *hades* is a pit called Tartarus, where the demons are chained. All of our souls will remain in *hades* from the time we die until the Judgment Day. At that point, our souls will be emptied out and we will be rejoined to our bodies and stand judgment. Those who are believers will go on to the Kingdom of God; those who are unbelievers will be tossed into Gehenna, also called the Lake of Fire or the Outer Darkness; it is a place designed to torture Satan and his angels, and is a place of horrible pain and anguish which lasts forever. Jesus, like all souls when He died, went to *hades*. He and the redeemed thief beside Him on the cross arrived (as do all righteous souls) in Paradise or Abraham's Side. Jesus, however, was allowed to cross the great chasm and spent three days preaching to the dead spirits on the other side of *hades*, in the hopes of saving some before the Judgment Day. After three days, Jesus was raised from the dead and God re-connected His soul to His body.

The above is one version, an example of what we called the Grave view in chapter five; this interpretation fits all of the thirteen canonical facts. There are many other interpretations, such as this example of the Paradise Previewed view:

When we die, our souls are separated from our bodies. Our souls go to Heaven or Hell, depending upon whether we were believers or not. Heaven is called Paradise or Abraham's Side; Hell is called *hades* or *sheol* or Tartarus or the Outer Darkness or the Lake of Fire. All terms essentially refer to only these two. Jesus, when He died, went to Hell. There He preached to the lost souls before rising from the Grave. Everyone stays in the spots where they will one day be, awaiting Judgment Day, when we will be reconnected with our bodies and then returned to our afterlife locations.

These are two examples of explanations which can well describe all of the facts with minimal assumptions. There are many others, of course, within the Christian fold, but the above are examples of typical, orthodox Christian approaches. Of those two, the former seems to me to be far more persuasive, but either fits the canonical facts and are acceptable belief systems.

Speculations

With so little information given to us, many theologians speculate (sometimes wildly) about how the facts fit together and about questions which are not at all discussed in the Scripture. For the most part I try to avoid such speculative questions, as they cannot be directly answered or explained by canon. However, two are particularly interesting and worthy of consideration.

What will the time in sheol/hades feel like?

The only Scriptural reference to the passage of time in *hades* is Jesus' parable about Abraham's Side. But as with all parables, we have to be careful not to stretch it too far, and make it say something more dogmatic than was intended. It seems safe to say that Abraham's Side is a place of peace and paradise, while the other side is a place of anguish.

Catholic theology contains a concept called *purgatory*, which we discussed briefly in chapter five. Purgatory is a process of purifying any sins away. Protestant theology says that when God views you during Judgment Day, your sinfulness simply ceases to exist (being "washed by the blood of Jesus" or, in my terminology, the waveform having collapsed), so there is no need to purify the sins while in *hades*. Catholics, however, see sins as being purified away while in *hades* so that when one is presented before God, there is no "sinful" waveform to collapse at all; we are presented as a pure bride, without blemish. This is not directly a Scriptural concept, but certainly fits well within the facts listed above and thus is within the realm of Scriptural possibility.

Unlike most Protestants, Luther taught a concept of "soul sleep," or *mortalism.* He argued that since the life of man is said to be in the blood (Lev

17:11), then the soul separated from the body would be lacking life. Thus our souls in *hades* are in a period of soul sleep, unable to note the passage of time. So even though they may spend millennia in *hades*, it will feel like only a moment has passed when they are raised from the dead. Mortalists argue that Luke 16 is a parable, and Jesus is not trying to give a literal description of *hades* but rather to demonstrate His point that those who end up outside of God's kingdom were well warned by Moses and the prophets, and received their just rewards on Earth.

Calvin and most other Protestant theologians strongly oppose this view, teaching something more similar to the Grave or Paradise Previewed views (which hold paradise as a place of comfort for the righteous and *hades* as a place of punishment for the wicked). Indeed it does seem difficult to me to explain how Jesus preached to imprisoned souls who were incapable of sensing or hearing Him.

Though I tend toward the view of Calvin in this case (rather than the Catholic or Lutheran view), we cannot know the truth with certainty. The Bible does not directly and factually make a statement one way or the other in this case.

What happens once you get to the lake of fire?

In addition, there has long been a debate among Christians over what happens at the Second Death, when the resurrected wicked have been cast into the lake of fire. Key to the debate is that we are never explicitly told that the wicked are tormented eternally in the lake of fire. We are told clearly that Satan, the beast, and the false prophet are tormented eternally (Rev 20:10, 14:9-11); we are further told that the "worms" of Gehenna never die and its fire burns eternally (Mark 9:43-48; Isa 66:24). When Jesus talks about people being thrown into the lake of fire it is associated with pain (Matt 13:42-50), and Matthew 25:41-46 says that those who are thrown into the lake of fire suffer eternal *punishment* but does not explicitly state that this is an eternal *burning torment* as received by Satan and his angels, simply that the punishment (separation from God) is eternal.

Most Christian theologians throughout history have the interpretation that this is eternal torturous punishment. There is good logical reason for this: if we are immortal beings and those going to heaven last immortally, then why would those in Gehenna not last immortally as well? For this reason, it has long been believed that those who end up in Gehenna suffer for their entire immortal life. This is called the **eternal torment** view of hell. It is probably conservative to say that upward of 95% of Christian theologians have held this view, and that it is generally considered the strongest Scriptural view. So this is the "default" or standard view of the lake of fire.

A minority view, but one which is also quite ancient (going back to such Christian heavyweights as Justin Martyr and Irenaeus) is a view called annihilationism. **Annihilationism** teaches that when the body and soul are thrown into Hell, they suffer only for a temporal period and then are destroyed. Their explanation of the Biblical facts is less orthodox, but also feasible from Scripture. They point out that the Bible does not explicitly state that humans will be tormented endlessly, only that Satan and his angels will. They point out that heaven is referred to as an eternal life, while being thrown into the lake of fire is called a "second death" (Rev 2:11). They also point out that almost exclusively, when the Bible talks about being thrown into the lake of fire they call it an act of destruction, not eternal torment: "broad is the road that leads to destruction" (Matt 7:13); God is the one who can "destroy both body and soul in hell" (Matt 10:28); and "they will be punished with everlasting destruction and shut out from the presence of the Lord" (2 Thess 1:9). This is a rare view, but does fit the Biblical canon facts and cannot be casually disregarded.

A far less common view, though one that became well known in light of Rob Bell's recent book *Love Wins*, is that of **Universal Salvation**. In this view, all those who are sent into the lake of fire will simply have their sins burned away, then be returned to God after. I cannot find many serious theologians throughout history who believe this, because it flies in the face of essentially every verse about Hell in the entire Scripture. Indeed, the verses like 2 Thess 1:9 and Matt 25:46 seem to be very definitive that there is no coming back from being thrown into the lake of fire; as such I will spend no more time on this view. As I said earlier, we must be open to any interpretations which explain the facts (like eternal torment and annilhilationism), but we can reject views like this one, which are unable to explain the facts (tempting though that is to wish it to be true).

Summary

In summary, we see that even with a relatively small amount of Scripture, we know quite a bit about what happens during the afterlife. We know that when we die, our souls are separated and we await judgment in *sheol/hades* (some say consciously, others not). We know that after Jesus returns, our bodies will be resurrected and will be rejoined to our souls. Those who had God's grace inside them as a spiritual force will find their names in the book of life; God's grace will overcome our spiritual gravity and we will become the eternal beings we were meant to be. (More on this in the next chapter.) Those who did not have God's grace, but relied upon their own willpower to make themselves "good people," will find that spiritual gravity has collapsed their souls until they have become beings of selfishness and rebellion, and they will be found guilty at the final judgment and cast with Satan into the lake of fire. At that point, either they will remain in eternal torment or will suffer proportionally to their sins and eventually be destroyed.

– SEVENTEEN –

THE RISE OF THE TIME LORDS

Thanks to my insistent sister-in-law, in 2011 I became a Whovian (the *Doctor Who* equivalent of a Trekkie). *Doctor Who*, the long-running British science fiction show, is a low-budget science fiction show which began in 1963. Originally the idea was to use time travel as a plot device for educational purposes, to teach about science and history to a family audience. The main character was a strange and mysterious man named simply, The Doctor; the title *Doctor Who* is a bit of a running gag, as characters will say, when introduced to him, "The Doctor? Doctor who?"

The show became quite successful, but after three years William Hartnell (the actor who played The Doctor), had to leave the show. As a plot device to keep the show going, the writers came up with the concept that The Doctor could regenerate into a new body with slight differences to personality. His basic outlook on life would remain the same, but his voice, body, and personality would differ slightly. This was an exceedingly clever idea at the time, and has become the central narrative device which has allowed *Doctor Who* to continue its story arc for literally multiple generations. The current star, Matt Smith, plays the Eleventh Doctor and was not born until *nineteen years* after the show debuted. This has allowed the series to keep alive the longest-running story arc in television history. The program was already quite old by the time the first Star Wars came out, and yet still today new *Doctor Who* episodes are being produced.

In the series, The Doctor is a Time Lord. The Time Lords are an ancient race of aliens who can travel through time and space and experience any time they wish. Their non-linear conception of time is a critical and central aspect of the show. The Doctor is a Time Lord who stole a TARDIS (Time And Relative Dimension in Space machine), which is a space-time traveling device disguised as a 1960s-era police callbox. The Doctor flies around in the TARDIS (which is "bigger on the inside," as a running show gag notes), accompanied by human companions. He was an integral player in a great war which ended in the destruction of the other Time Lords. Now he travels back and forth through time and space, observing and (often) interfering with the lives of humans and aliens. Consider it a geekier version of *Quantum Leap*, where Dr. Sam Beckett traveled through time "righting wrongs."

The Doctor is not the only master of time, however; the TARDIS itself has a personality, and in one memorable 2011 episode was placed into human form. The TARDIS, even more than the Time Lords, sees time as simply another dimension of space; as such, she is both able to tell the future and struggles greatly with concepts such as past and future, frequently confusing the words.

What is intriguing about the Time Lords is imagining a being who, rather than being trapped in our limited perceptions, can actually understand time and see its true nature. For most of history, man has viewed the universe as a three-dimensional universe (left/right, up/down, in/out) which is evolving from an initial condition to an end condition. Time is pictured as a sort of river in which we all ride, moving from one moment in time to another.

One of the most fascinating impacts of the discoveries of quantum mechanics is that this is most certainly not the way the universe actually works! This view of time is simply a limitation of our brain's perceptive abilities. It turns out that the laws of physics work perfectly fine whether you start at the beginning of the universe or the end; that is, the laws of physics are essentially reversible and could have run in either direction. As such, physicists would say that there really is no "past" and no "future"; everything simply is the way that it is, and it is our perception which changes. Recall our earlier discussion about quantum mechanics, where Lloyd says that you have already made every choice in your life, you simply have not yet experienced making it.

I think that an example will help. Imagine that I have a baseball. I take this baseball and place it on our piece of two-dimensional paper, Flatland. Now let us say that I bring this baseball to life, and give it the powers of perception of the world around it; however, I limit the "perception" aspect of its personality to the boundaries of Flatland. That is, even though the reality of the baseball is that it is a three-dimensional sphere, it is only capable of perceiving two dimensions of itself (whatever is touching Flatland) at a given moment.

To the baseball, then, life begins the moment it began to touch the paper. This is its birth day, the day that it first was able to perceive. At this time, it sees itself as a small circle. Then I push the ball into the paper and it begins to move through the paper, so that the paper is slicing it in half perhaps a quarter of an inch higher. From the baseball's perspective, it is now a larger circle; the small circle that it "was" has already happened, and it does not know what shape it will take in the future. As the baseball continues to pass through the paper during its life, the ball perceives itself as circles growing larger and larger all the way until mid-life, when the paper is cutting the baseball exactly in half. Then, as its life continues, the circle again shrinks smaller and smaller as it ages. Eventually, as the baseball passes out the other side of the paper, it now ceases to exist in Flatland. This is the death of it—as far as the baseball can tell, at least.

But remember that at all times, the baseball was still a baseball, wasn't it? At mid-life, when the baseball perceived itself as a large circle on Flatland, it thought of its small circle birthday as "past," and its small-circle death day as "future." But in reality, *it was the same ball at all times*. It never ceased to be the one coherent solid object. It was not a small circle which "aged" into a large circle and then back to a small circle, was it? No, but because its perception was bound to the two-dimensional Flatland, it was never able to experience more than a cross-section of itself at a given time.

This example well illustrates the results of being a creature whose perception is bound to a particular set of dimensions. Just like the baseball, our perception is trapped. We are four-dimensional beings who can only perceive of a single three-dimensional cross section at a time. The future is unknown only in that it has not yet been observed; it already exists (just as the "top" of the baseball always existed), but we have not yet perceived it, being bound as we are to our three-dimensional world.

As Einstein put it, physics seems to be telling us that we are actually living in a four-dimensional universe, not a three-dimensional universe which is "evolving through time." It is just that we can only perceive of these three dimensions, so we only see one "slice" of ourselves at a time.

So, back to *Doctor Who*. The Doctor is able to perceive of all different states of time. To the Time Lords, there is no such thing as an unchangeable past and a controllable present and a semi-controllable future; rather, there simply is the thing called Reality, which humans (as three-dimensional beings subject to entropy) can only perceive in one "cross-section" at a time, moving from a state of low entropy to high entropy. That is, his companions are bound to see along time's arrow, while The Doctor is not. And he travels around through space-time to see what all he can see.

Not only did we see that our perception of time "passing by" us is little more but a limitation of our perceptive abilities, also recall that Einstein's relativity also showed us that the rate of time is not perceived the same on different objects. Relativity shows that at very high velocities or under very high gravity, time is experienced more slowly by the person experiencing it. That is, the atoms of an atomic clock literally degrade at different rates whether they are on top of the mountain or at the foot of the mountain; they degrade differently whether rocketing through space or standing in the space station.

The key point is to understand that our perception of time is not reality, but is completely a fabrication *of the universe in which we live.* The "real you" is a combination of all of the moments of your life, all existing as part of your fourth-dimensional reality simultaneously. Unfortunately your brain is limited, and can only perceive of the three dimensions which you can directly experience at this moment. You can experience only one cross-section of the "true you" at any given time—and because of relativity, our cross-sections are not even all consistently spaced apart, but rather differ from person to person depending upon gravity and speed of motion!

+ + + theology: the Kingdom of God + + +

Last chapter, we saw that an understanding of the actual facts of the Bible were important to understanding the concept of Hell. We saw that the afterlife was actually much more complex than simply dying and waking up either on a cloud or in a fire; there is an intermediate period of soul separation, followed by a resurrection of the body and judgment, and ultimately those who choose to be judged based upon their own merits instead of Christ's merits find themselves cast into Gehenna, the lake of fire, for punishment.

When it comes to Heaven, people's opinions are less muddled, simply because the Bible does not talk about Heaven as much as it talks about Hell. But still, let us clear up a few things.

First, there is a difference in Scripture between "Heaven" and the "Kingdom of Heaven/Kingdom of God." Today the universe that we live in is described in the Bible as having three parts: *hades* (the land of the dead), Earth (the land of the living), and Heaven (the land of the eternals—God and the angels). So "Heaven," properly speaking, is the place where God and the angels live; for clarity I will call this the Throne Room. The Throne Room is not where our spirits go when we die; they go to the part of *hades* where righteous souls await judgment.

After the resurrection and the Judgment, the Bible tells us very specifically what will happen, in Revelations 21-22.

First, in Rev 21:1, we find out that this universe is destroyed. We are told specifically, "the first heaven and the first earth had passed away, and the sea was no more." The word "sea" here is *thalassa*, and to understand it we must read its context; a few verses earlier, this word is equated to *hades* (Rev 20:13—"and the sea gave up the dead who were in it, Death and *hades* gave up the dead who were in them"). This is echoed in 2 Pet 3:10, where Peter tells us that the universe will be destroyed upon God's return by a holy fire, and both heaven and earth will disappear.

So we know that this original three-part universe (heaven/earth/*hades*) will be destroyed. And then we are told that a "new heaven and a new earth" are created, with a new and holy Jerusalem being made (Rev 21:1-2). We are told that God Himself will dwell with man; no longer will God dwell in the heavens but on Earth (Rev 21:2-3). The Bible says that in this New Jerusalem, there will be no more death or pain, for the new universe is made differently and "the former things have passed away" (Rev 21:4-5). Those people who believed in God and whose name were in the book of life are here, while the others suffered the Second Death via the lake of fire (as in the last chapter; see also Rev 21:8).

Then John is shown New Jerusalem, which he tries to describe. His description makes it roughly the size of Europe, and he compares all of it to shining jewels. Some take this quite literally (the gates made of pearl, the streets made of actual gold, the sea made of crystals), but more likely John was just doing the best he could in human words to describe something which was indescribable. Unlike Old Jerusalem, there is no Temple, for there is no need for sacrifice: God Himself and Jesus are present and dwelling with men. There are also no sun or moon, and all light comes directly from God's presence. (Rev 21:10-27).

On these points basically all Christians agree, with only minor disagreements about how literally John's description of New Jerusalem should be taken. But what is of interest to me are a few very clear statements which show that physics is fundamentally different in this new creation:

- Our current universe is destroyed (Rev 21:1);

- The new universe is more than three-dimensional, for God Himself is able to live in it with us (Rev 21:2-3);

- We are able to interact with God as He is, not simply one aspect of Him (Rev 21:3);

- Death no longer exists (Rev 21:4);

- Pain and suffering no longer exist (Rev 21:4);

- All things are made new and pure (Rev 21:5,27);

- The sun and moon do not exist, nor are they necessary (Rev 21:23);

- There is no nighttime (Rev 21:25); and

- The new universe is eternal (Matt 6:19; Heb 10:34; 1 Pet 1:4; 1 Thess 4:17; many others)

What is interesting to me about this is that there are two clear conclusions as a physics geek: (1) *there is no Second Law of Thermodynamics in the new universe*; and (2) *it is at least a four-dimensional universe, in which we are capable of perceiving all four dimensions.*

Of course it is completely possible for God to make the new universe however He likes, with whatever laws He prefers. He is not "fixing" the old world, but destroying it and recreating it.

We know that there cannot be any Second Law of Thermodynamics in this world, for several reasons. First, an eternal universe is impossible with entropy in effect, for entropy demands that the energy of the universe must eventually dissipate into the lowest possible energy state, a "heat death" where no motion or work is possible. Second, we know that the new earth has no sun and therefore no outside energy coming into the system; this makes New Jerusalem an isolated system, so entropy would always increase if the Second Law remained in effect. This in turn means that decay and death would be inevitable, and we are explicitly told that this will not occur.

Revelation makes it clear that there is no Second Law of Thermodynamics in the Kingdom of God; the claims it makes are not possible unless either the Second Law is invalidated, or if an outside source of energy is provided (and we are explicitly told that no outside source is present, only God who is inside with us).

We also know that it is impossible for the new universe to be merely a three-dimensional universe like this one. Recall that we live in at least a four-dimensional universe, but are only capable of perceiving it in three dimensional cross-sections. Thus the real "you" looks a lot different than the way you view yourself. Just as, in our example, our baseball saw himself as two-dimensional circles which changed over time, we see ourselves as three-dimensional humans who change over time. The reality, though, is that you are a single four dimensional creature: simultaneously a baby and a teenager and a thirty-something and a sixty-year old and a dying person. All times of your life are equally real and equally present; you are simply limited to perceiving them one three-dimensional slice at a time.

Since we are told in Revelation 21 that we will be with God, that the new universe can contain God, and that we will be able to perceive Him directly, then we know that we can no longer be bound by the three-dimensional perception limitation that plagues us today.

So we may be confident that the new universe will be one of at least four dimensions, and one in which there is no Second Law of Thermodynamics and, therefore, no entropy.

The End of Entropy, or: How We All Become Time Lords

The Bible does not tell us much about New Jerusalem, the "Kingdom of God." It makes it very clear that this is where we want to end up, to be sure; and it makes the alternative look pretty obviously bad by comparison. But I think we can reasonably guess a few things, based upon our newfound knowledge that there is no entropy, and that we are no longer bound to three-dimensional perception.

We have all heard others ask—and probably wondered ourselves—if Heaven will be boring. I mean, what exactly will we be *doing*? Standing around worshipping God for billions of years sounds a bit dull, no matter how "holier than thou" you want to act.

But fear not – because if we live in a four-dimensional (or higher) universe, and we are not subject to the effects of entropy, then the result is quite amazing.

Without entropy, there is no time's arrow. There is no sensing of one moment being "before" any others. Recall our baseball analogy. Without a concept of entropy, no one moment of his life is any more "present" than any other: past, present, and future are all equally "now" to him.

In addition, now that we live in four-dimensional Timeland, rather than three-dimensional Spaceland, when we look in the mirror we see our *true* selves, not just a three-dimensional cross section. When our baseball came to Spaceland and looked in the mirror, he saw a sphere rather than a series of circles, didn't he? In the same way, when you are in Timeland, a mirror will show *all* of you, not just a cross-section of moments.

If you looked in a four-dimensional mirror, you would quite literally see yourself as simultaneously the baby being cuddled and the six year old at Disney and the teenager studying for his final and the college kid on a date and the twenty-something being married and the thirty-something tucking in their boy and the fifty-something bouncing his grandkid on your knee and the sixty-something retiring and traveling the world. All parts of your history are present and real and you will perceive all of them at once.

Have you ever had a moment where you wished, with everything in your heart, that you could hold your child again as an infant and hear him coo at you? Have you ever wished that you could always remember the look of joy on your child's face on Christmas morning? Have you ever wished that you could recapture the romantic feeling of your wedding day (or night)? Have you ever wished, as you kissed your son's forehead good night and smelled his hair, you could make this moment last forever?

Good news. You can.

If we are freed from our three-dimensional perceptive limitations, and if we have no time arrow, then all moments will be equally present to us. For eternity, you literally will be able to exist in all moments of your life, experiencing everything which made you, you. And even better, all of the sinfulness was eliminated by the Cross, so it is truly nothing but joy and perfection.

Still, will we eventually get bored? Nope. No chance. What is boredom? It is an emotion which arises when time is passing during a period that we do not find interesting. But remember that in the Kingdom of God, time does not pass! As Time Lords, time is just another dimension to us, one we can walk through as easily as we can walk up stairs. Today if you take measurements for a coat, you have to account for your height (first dimension), width (second dimension), and thickness (third dimension). In the Kingdom of God, you would also have to be measured for a fourth dimension—time. Time is just as much a part of your physical measurements as your height, width, and thickness.

What would you think if someone came to you and said, "Won't it feel tall to be a normal height?" You would think they were crazy, and keep a hand on your wallet. The same is true when you ask if you will be bored in heaven: if you look in the mirror, you will see your "time" dimension in the same way as you see your height, width, or thickness. You will not be bored because there is no "time" passing by. Your entire past, present, and future are all present to you. There is not past or present or future, only "Now." Just this moment. It will feel exactly like any moment of your life, but it will never have an ending. Without entropy or decay, and without being trapped as a three-dimensional perceptive being, you will not feel time passing at all.

When our baseball moved from Flatland into Spaceland, he no longer felt himself evolving as a series of circles: when he looked in the mirror, he saw not a series of circles but a complete Sphere. He saw a single being, all of the circular "moments" of his life made into one coherent whole. In the same way, you will no longer perceive your life as a series of moments strung together, but as one coherent, solid whole: a Time Lord, past/present/future all at once. You will be complete and the way that you are meant to be, experiencing everything you have ever experienced, all at once. (Or, as the Tenth Doctor described it, you will be all "Wibbly-wobbly timey-wimey.")

The true and complete "you" will be able to dine with the true and complete Abraham, the true and complete Jacob, the true and complete Paul, and your true and complete family and friends. All will sit and share a glass of wine in that new kingdom together.

You will be able to experience tucking in your kids again (moving in the fourth dimension) just as directly as you can experience jumping today (moving in the third dimension).

As great as this seems, when that day comes there is something which will give you even more joy. It may not seem possible, but it is true: even as great as it sounds to re-experience all of your life's joy, you will experience an even greater joy. Any Christian has experienced those few moments of existentially pure communion with God: those moments where we feel as though we are one with Him, whether it be during a moving time of prayer or a wonderful singing experience or viewing a beautiful landscape or hearing a brilliant sermon which elevates your mind so that you feel you are just on the edge of really talking to God. Those few moments of pure joy will be our entire eternity, for as we are there, timelessly, we will be in communion with God.

There will be no end or beginning. There will be no aging or boredom. In that Kingdom, we all become Time Lords. In that Kingdom, God has freed us from our exile on earth, has destroyed the laws of entropy, has broken the shackles which bind our spiritual perception to these three dimensions, and has placed us in New Jerusalem with Him, the Lord of Lords, forever.

CONCLUSION

Geeks often feel left out of Christianity. Their love of science is seen as dangerous; their love of asking tough questions is viewed as a challenge to the legitimacy of the faith. When they go to read books about their faith, they find either fluff or detailed seminary-level theology which fails to inspire and excite them. This is ironic, because a sci-fi geek can understand an awful lot about Christian theology, in a very exciting way, as I hope I have shown.

The purpose of this book was to inspire you to think about theology in fresh ways, to use my experiences as a geek and an engineer to try and see God in a fresh light, and excite the geeks of the world with the truths contained in Scripture. Everything I said in here was meant to be an analogy or a thought experiment; I dare not claim it to be true, but rather written in an attempt to help you see the universe in new ways and be excited about the amazing and awe-inspiring spiritual world our God built for us.

If something I wrote did not help you, throw it out. Ignore it and move on. I am little more than a cymbal clanging loudly, and if the notes do not help you hear God's music better, then forget it.

For all of you theologians who wish I would have spent more time fleshing out some of the theology...tough. I warned you up front that I was a "horse is a sphere" kind of guy; I wanted to illustrate the principles, not teach a class. I hope the book was enjoyable and thought provoking for you. If not, and you want some real theology, then go read N.T. Wright, Michael Horton, or someone far more qualified than I to write such a book.

I hope our discussion about extra-dimensionality can help you understand that God can be Three-in-One just as well as a Pringles can is simultaneously a circle, a front rectangle and a side rectangle—and that the Persons of God (Father, Son and Spirit) can no more be separated than the "Pringles can" is still a can if you cut it up into a circle and two rectangles.

I hope our discussion of the creativity of engineering helps you understand the amazing fine-tuning God did in the universe, that His role as our Creator is undeniable and beautifully elegant.

I hope our discussion about the principles of stellar formation help you picture how your own actions lead to a spiritual gravity which by its nature tends to collapse infinitely inward toward selfishness, and can only be counteracted if an internal sort of heat (the grace of God) is given to offset the spiritual gravitation of your sins.

I hope our discussion about supply and demand helps you understand how the Law both simultaneously shows us how to live and condemns us for our inability to live in such a manner.

I hope our discussion of the Sims helps you marvel, as I do, that God would love us and care about us this deeply, and to understand the nature of the man.

I hope our discussion about engineering specifications and the criticality of being exacting helps you understand the Moral Law, and how we have made our souls non-conforming product which deserves to be scrapped.

I hope our discussion of composites helps you understand the hypostatic union, and how Jesus can be both fully God and fully man.

I hope that our discussion about reinforcing out of spec components helps you understand the truth of the Gospel, the good news that our justification before God comes not from us having to "rework ourselves," but from Jesus being sent as a reinforcement to take the load of the Law off of us.

I hope our discussion of heat transfer helps you picture that God's grace is sent to us not by our own actions but by a sort of convection, that it is our physical connection to Jesus through the Holy Spirit by which the grace of God flows.

I hope our discussion of Schrodinger's Cat helps you understand why, even after salvation, you remain a sinner; and gives you confidence that, at the Great White Throne where you are Observed, God will see your duality collapse into pure righteousness of Christ.

I hope our discussion about entropy helps you see why it is right to reject me-first, American-style, "pick-yourself-up-by-your-bootstraps," self-help Christianity: that is the way of Law and works and death, not the way of receiving God's pure grace.

I hope our discussion of quantum mechanics helps you see that the predestination versus free will debate is a bit silly and short-sighted, and is based upon our faulty perception that we truly exist only in this moment; instead, I hope you embrace the concept that your choices have all been made by you and now it is time to reveal them to yourself.

I hope our discussion of geek show tie-ins helps illustrate the importance of deciding exactly how we interpret Scripture, and how much weight to give non-canonical works.

I hope our discussion about atomic structure helps you see how heresy is the adding to or taking away from the twenty-five key fundamentals of the Gospel, but that within the bounds of Christianity there is some legitimate room for variation.

I hope our study of relativity helps you learn not to judge others, and to fully accept that your sin was just as demanding of Christ's death as the murderer next door.

I hope our discussion the retcon process and the R2D2 spy theory helps you get a good vision of what the Bible does truly say about the afterlife and Hell, instead of worrying about and arguing about different interpretations of those facts.

I hope our discussion of Doctor Who and a four-dimensional world without entropy helps you picture what heaven might be like, and how an eternal world stripped of the Second Law of thermodynamics and unbound by our current perceptional limitations is something for which we can yearn.

But most of all, I hope this book made you think. We are told in the Scriptures to love God with all of our heart, all of our mind, and all of our strength; we are not to forget the "mind" part of this command. God did not, as Galileo once famously said, give us the ability to reason and then forbid us to use it. Far from it, He desires that we use our brains to grow closer to Him.

Even if we are all just a bunch of geeks.

ACKNOWLEDGEMENTS

It would be impossible for me to acknowledge everyone who has been a help in getting me to this point, so I am only going to name the few who carried the heavy lifting. But to all the rest of you who inspire me and encourage me daily, and to all of my regular readers on my (now long-since-abandoned) blog, I give a sincere "Thank you"—I am at times quite lazy, and without the encouragement and feedback I would never have made it.

I thank my wife, Jessica, for her amazing support in all areas of my life. Her incredible patience alone is admirable. The fact that she actually actively listens and engages me in discussions of theological philosophy and science (neither of which are her favorite subjects) is flat-out incredible. I am not worthy to be her husband.

I would like to thank Niki Zimmerman, who was a friend even before she became family. She is an amazing encourager, and I honestly see her as the sister I never had. Her work on this book was absolutely critical to making it resemble an actual cohesive document rather than a few engineering sketches and disjointed thoughts.

I would like to thank Joshua Hurlburt. The first inkling of writing this book started with him and I discussing a blog post I wrote about the impact of quantum mechanics on the fate/free will debate, which you of course now know turned into a chapter in this book.

Finally I would like to thank Sara Bowyer. It was Sara who said to me one Sunday before church, as I struggled with whether to write this book, "I really love the way you write. You seriously should consider writing a book. You would do great at it."

If you hated the book, you likely are not still reading. But if you hated this book and for some reason you are still reading, these people share the blame: they are the ones whom God put in my life to be a light and an encouragement, and from whom I found my voice.

ABOUT THE AUTHOR

Michael Belote is an engineer and data scientist who lives in Little Rock, Arkansas with his wonderful wife and two wild and crazy sons.

Michael received a B.Sc. in Industrial Engineering and an M.Sc. in Operations Management from the College of Engineering at the University of Arkansas. (Go Hogs!) He also received a Post-Master's in Data Science from Johns Hopkins.

In his career he apprenticed in the automotive and electronics industry, worked in the ammunition industry for a few years full-time, and has worked for a Fortune 10 company ever since, as a Director of manufacturing engineering and data science in their Wind Energy division.

As a college engineering student, Michael became a born-again Christian and threw himself into Bible study and theological books to try and make some sense of his newfound faith. Throughout his young Christian life, he tried his hand at Catholic, Methodist, Southern Baptist, and Missionary Baptist churches, while reading theologies of Augustine, Aquinas, Luther, Calvin, and many more. He eventually found a home at Grace Church in Little Rock, where he has served for many years on the Elder Board and delivering sermons as a member of the Teaching team.

He is also weirdly obsessed with science fiction, fantasy football, modern physics, and ante-Nicene Near Eastern history. Pray for his wife.

RELEVANT SOURCE MATERIAL

Bercot, D., ed., 1998. A Dictionary of Early Christian Beliefs, Hendrickson Publishers.

Blocker, J., 1989. American Temperance Movements: Cycles of Reform, Twayne Publishers.

Bryanton, R. 2007. Imagining the Tenth Dimension: A New Way of Thinking About Time and Space, Trafford Publishing.

Calvin, J., 2007. Institutes of the Christian Religion, Hendrickson.

Carroll, S. "Ten Things Everyone Should Know About Time," Discover Magazine, blogs.discovermagazine.com/cosmicvariance/2011/09/01/ten-things-everyone-should-know-about-time/, (2011).

Catechism of the Catholic Church, numerous articles.

Chester, M., 1987. Primer of Quantum Mechanics, John Wiley.

Crockett, W.,ed. Four Views on Hell.

Davies, P. "How bio-friendly is the universe?" International Journal of Astrobiology, vol. 2, no. 2 (2003).

Deem, R. "Is our copy of the Bible a reliable copy of the original?" www.godandscience.org/apologetics/bibleorg.html

DeSilva, D., 2000. Honor, Patronage, Kinship, & Purity, IVP Academic.

Dirac, P., 1930. The Principles of Quantum Mechanics, International Series of Monograms on Physics.

Easton, M., 2000. Easton's Bible Dictionary, Christian Classics Ethereal Library.

Edmundson, G., 2000. The Church in Rome in the First Century, Christian Classics Ethereal Library.

Erickson, M.J., 1998. Christian Theology, 2nd Ed., Baker Academic.

Einstein, A., 2007. Relativity, the Special and General Theory, Second Ed., Pearson.

Faye, J. "Copenhagen Interpretation of Quantum Mechanics," Stanford Encyclopedia of Philosophy (2008).

Ferguson, E., 2003. Backgrounds of Early Christianity: Third Edition, William B. Eerdmans Publishing.

Feynman, R., 1965. The Feynman Lectures on Physics, Addison-Wesley.

Feynman, R., 1985. QED: The Strange Theory of Light and Matter, Princeton University Press.

Goldstein, M., 1993. The Refrigerator and the Universe, Harvard.

Hawking, S., 1998. A Brief History of Time, Bantam.

Hey, A. and Walters, P., 2003. The New Quantum Universe, Cambridge Univ. Press.

Holding, J., 2009. Trusting the New Testament, Xulon.

Holy Bible, English Standard Version ESV. (2001). Crossway.

HyperPhysics, Georgia State University, numerous articles.

Jeffers, J., 1999. The Greco-Roman World of the New Testament Era, Intervarsity Press.

Kitchen, K., 1966. Ancient Orient and Old Testament, Inter-Varsity Press.

Kohler, K., 2011. Jewish Theology, Amazon Digital Services.

Lewis, C., 1946. The Great Divorce, HarperSanFrancisco.

Lewis, C., 1952. Mere Christianity, HarperOne.

Liu, C. 2008. The Three Body Problem.

Luther, M., 1823. Martin Luther on the Bondage of the Will: Written in Answer to the Diatribe of Erasmus on Free-Will, T. Bensley.

Margeneau, H., 1950. The Nature of Physical Reality, McGraw-Hill.

Mehra, J., 1982. The historical development of quantum theory, Springer-Verlag.

Metzger, B., 2005. The Text of the New Testament, Oxford Press.

Moore, W., 1992. Schrodinger: Life and Thought, Cambridge Univ. Press.

NIV Archaeological Study Bible. (2005). Zondervan.

Ortberg, J., 2009. The Me I Want To Be: Becoming God's Best Version of You, Zondervan.

Peacock, J., 1999. Cosmological Physics, Cambridge University.

Peterson, A., 1968. Quantum Physics and the Philosophical Tradition, MIT Press.

Petroski, H., 1982. To Engineer is Human, Vintage Books.

Pressense, E., 1870. The Early Years of Christianity: The Apostolic Era, Christian Classics Ethereal Library.

Rees, M., 1999. Just Six Numbers, Harper-Collins.

Richardson, C., 1909. Early Christian Fathers, Christian Classics Ethereal Library.

Sawyer, R., 2009. Flashforward, Tor Books.

Schaff, P., 1882. History of the Christian Church, Vol I: Apostolic Christianity. AD 1-100. Christian Classics Ethereal Library.

Schaff, P., 1882. History of the Christian Church, Vol II: Ante-Nicene Christianity. AD 100-325. Christian Classics Ethereal Library.

Schaff, P., 1882. History of the Christian Church, Vol III: Nicene and Post-Nicene Christianity. AD 325-600. Christian Classics Ethereal Library.

Schaff, P., 1882. History of the Christian Church, Vol IV: Medieval Christianity. AD 590-1073. Christian Classics Ethereal Library.

Schrodinger, E. "The present situation in quantum mechanics," translated by Trimmer, J., Proceedings of the American Philosophical Society.

Schroeder, G., 1997. The Science of God, Broadway Books.

Stevenson, R., 1991. Dr Jekyll and Mr Hyde, Dover Publications.

Tipler, F., 2007. The Physics of Christianity, Doubleday.

Tipler, P., 1998. Physics for Scientists and Engineers, Vol. 1: Mechanics, Oscillations, and Waves, Thermodynamics., W.H. Freeman.

Tipler, P., 1998. Physics for Scientists and Engineers, Vol. 2: Electricity and Magnetism, Light, W.H. Freeman.

Tipler, P., 1998. Physics for Scientists and Engineers, Vol. 3: Modern Physics, Quantum Mechanics, Relativity, & The Structure of Matter, W.H. Freeman.

Wimmel, H. "Quantum physics and observed reality," World Scientific (1992).

www.arrowheadradiator.com

www.wikipedia.org, numerous articles

Made in the USA
Coppell, TX
10 October 2020